THIS IS THE END... MY ONLY FRIEND

LIVING AND DYING WITH JIM MORRISON

THIS IS THE END...
MY ONLY FRIEND

LIVING AND DYING
WITH JIM MORRISON

JUDY HUDDLESTON

SHAPOLSKY PUBLISHERS, INC.
NEW YORK

A Shapolsky Book

For any additional information, contact:
Shapolsky Publishers, Inc.
136 West 22nd Street
New York, NY 10011
(212) 633-2022
FAX (212) 633-2123

10 9 8 7 6 5 4 3 2 1

ISBN 1-56171-038-5

Design and Typography by Owl Graphics, New York

Manufactured in the United States of America

For my mother . . .

The days are bright and filled with pain,
Enclose me in your gentle rain.
The time you ran was too insane.
We'll meet again, we'll meet again.

from Jim Morrison's
"The Crystal Ship"

My thanks to my mother and father for always loving me; Jim Morrison for his spirit; Glen Mensing for believing in me; Linda Heet Cateriano for reminding me of my heart; Laurens Schwartz for his perseverance with this book; Michelle Orwin for rescuing the manuscript; Donn Teal for help in editing; Lois Condon and Larry Meltzer for sustaining me last year; Robert Ketchum for completing the circle; Shadow for unconditional love – and to God, for existence.

CONTENTS

PROLOGUE

I WAS SEVENTEEN WHEN I FELL IN LOVE with the singer. At the end of an old, green cracked pier in Venice, in a club renovated with fake cheetah skins, the spotlight shot through the dark blue silence to the dimming stage and caught Jim stepping up to the microphone. He paused inside the enchanted circle, in a dazzling new kingdom, and the reigning color, light, and sound had a mad poet to direct our sensations.

The soft white light played over Jim's face and held it. Aware of the spell his beauty cast, he surveyed his audience, then closed his eyes until his delicately destructible features drew an involuntary soft sigh, an audible breath of life that he gathered into himself. Then, transformed by the moment, he opened his eyes and began to sing. As in a polite introduction to magic, no drawbacks were mentioned . . .

The Doors and getting high seemed to happen simultaneously. It's as if the world of childhood and our parents had ended, and this was the new world. With all the intensity with which I renounced my first sixteen years and the beliefs I inherited, I now embraced the revolution.

My parents had just been through a very unhappy, alcoholic divorce. As an only child, I was torn between my liberal mother and conservative father. Considering the political climate, I rebelled against my dad so totally that we barely spoke until my mid-twenties. But I don't think it's a coincidence that my father was also a darkly handsome, blue-eyed singer and had been with a popular band in his youth.

I spent the first eleven months of 1967 trekking across cities, a new Bacchante still following her ancient god. I left my boyfriend, the human race, and reality. There was only Jim.

During the last year of high school, my girlfriend Linda and I left the safe suburbs of Orange County for Los Angeles every weekend. We went to see The Doors, a local band which had just come out with its first single. We usually ended up on the Sunset Strip, at Gazzarri's, the Hullabaloo, or the Whisky A Go-Go, but we sometimes found oursleves in Santa Monica, Pasadena, West Covina, or Anaheim. We met Ronnie, Rich, and Bill, nice guys who were about our age and worked as roadies for The Doors. They were fun to hang out with, and we could always get back stage. Ronnie was the guitarist's brother, and Rich and Bill were college students; Bill later became The Doors' manager.

After school and on weekends when nothing was happening, we'd get The Doors' first album and play it over and over. We'd smoke a lot of amazingly cheap grass and go off into another world. I remember staring at Jim's face, his words embedding themselves in my mind for hours. I was reading a lot of Aldous Huxley, William Blake, and Alan Watts, but to me Jim summarized and went beyond them. The world was changing fast, but Jim seemed to be one step ahead.

I knew about Pam from the beginning, but I felt my perseverance would win in the end. I'd had pretty good luck with guys, and I naïvely assumed this would just take a little time. I learned to wait – something I unfortunately became very good at doing. I have never again loved anyone like I loved Jim. I'll never know exactly why I fell so hard, fast, and totally for him, nor why I never gave up on him when any sane person would have.

I wrote the first draft of this book when I was in my early twenties. Though I've been over it several times since then, I've tried to stay as close to the truth as the original. It's not the kind of thing adulthood can improve. In many ways, life just happens and we're powerless over the outcome. The rest is history.

This is mine.

I DIDN'T BREAK DOWN UNTIL JIM HAD been dead four years. I didn't know I'd half believed the rumors that Jim was alive until Pam died of an overdose. There is no way she would die if he was still on the planet. When I left for Paris, I felt haunted. Not long after I returned, everything caught up with me. It was not only the end of Jim's life, but the end of my conflicted childhood, the end of the '60s, and the end of many romantic ideals.

I graduated from Choinard (which had become Cal Arts), but I didn't know how to make a living as an artist. Needless to say, I was in therapy for years. I traveled, wrote, made art, worked at straight jobs, and did lots of drugs. I lived with a couple of guys, went to graduate school, taught, wrote, made more art, eventually married – and continued taking drugs. You can't take Valium for twenty years and stop by yourself. My husband and I finally decided to separate, and I checked into a hospital for chemical dependency . . .

When I heard Oliver Stone was going to direct a film about Jim and The Doors, I was both excited and scared. As one of Jim's countless romantic interests, I was found by his researchers. After my first meeting with Oliver, his producer asked me to work as a technical advisor on his movie. Once we had agreed, I walked out of the office and Oliver appeared. He gave me a hug and said, "I loved your manuscript. But it'll be a hard sell." I didn't mention how long I'd been trying.

Oliver introduced me to Val Kilmer, who had been chosen to play Jim. He was tall, with beautiful, friendly eyes and hair dyed black. I liked him on sight. He moved a lot like Jim, but he didn't seem quite "dangerous" enough; there was something about him that projected a fundamental decency. After introducing me to the other actors, Oliver took us on a tour of the building.

The prop room was full of American flags, "antique" '60s furniture, posters, and lots of vintage clothes. I imagined the times filtering through an underground of hand-me-downs until resurrected as movie props. Another room was filled with psychedelic light-show posters. "I didn't like those the first time," I said.

"Remember, they don't look good until they're under a white light. Then they're three-dimensional and seem to move," the prop woman reminded me.

I still thought those posters were for people who didn't take enough acid. Otherwise, all you needed was a blank wall.

Oliver guided us into another room where photo-graphs of The Doors were hung in chronological sequence and tagged with titles. Swatches of cloth were attached beneath the shots, so the designer would know what to do. Val walked down the rogue's gallery and paused before a picture of the bloated late-Jim.

"It's like he aged twenty years in five," he com-mented.

"Yeah, I know." I walked back to Jim's earlier "young lion" phase photos. "I like his early-middle stage the best," I said.

Val said he did, too. "I *hate* that jacket," he moaned, indicating one of early-Jim's pea coats. He hid the photo half under another, hoping he wouldn't have to wear it.

"How old do you think Jim was?" Val asked.

"About twelve to fourteen," I said.

"I've been trying for about fourteen to sixteen," he said.

"In A.A., they say that you stop developing at the age you started using drugs." We agreed that Jim couldn't have made it too far past fourteen.

Later, I was alone with Oliver. "You know, the thing I forgot to tell you last time was that Jim was really romantic," I said.

"I got a good sense of that in your book," Oliver nodded. "He really had a thing about red-haired, Irish Amazons," he added.

"I'm Scottish," I said. Actually, I was remembering he had told me Jim was like a mirror, and everyone had a different impression of him. It occurred to me I was the romantic one, not Jim.

A few weeks later, Val asked me to come by the band's rehearsal at a sound studio. His sideburns and hair had grown out, and the way he held the microphone was just like Jim. It was so unnerving, I had to keep looking away. They kept playing the same phrases over and over, first using Jim's original, then Val singing live. They used playback from The Doors, but it just sounded like synthesized drumbeats to me. All that repetitious switching from past to present struck me as a difficult way to be creative.

"What do you think?" Oliver asked as I was leaving.

"Well, it's not as shocking," I said.

"It can't be," he said. "It's been twenty years."

"No, I mean seeing Val as Jim," I explained.

"How do you think he's doing?"

"Really well. He reminds me of the best part of Jim. The part I loved." I looked aside for a moment. "He's moving just right," I said, trying to sound professional. "Something about the muscles in his thighs."

"What about the sexuality?" Oliver asked.

"I don't know . . . about that," I said.

"You should find out," he said – half joking, I suspected – and laughed. But as I walked outside, I realized the biggest difference between the '90s and the '60s was that I never would find out. And sometimes, like then, I would give anything for the bad old days . . .

Judy Huddleston
Los Angeles
1991

CHAPTER 1

SOMEBODY TO LOVE

IT IS NIGHT. GARNISHED IN BRIGHT SILKS, satins and feathers, people drift through the warm December darkness. Alone in my car, I'm dizzily soothed and madly intoxicated by vodka and expectations. Laughter wafts like pale, colored smoke, floating into my dream. I feel the hopeful energy sink into mine, stirring the contagious spirit that precedes any performance, yet making this appearance of The Doors at the Shrine seem unique unto itself.

Deciding it's time to go backstage, I am prepared to use my slickly incoherent version of a dumb blonde if worse comes to worse. But tonight my embroidered clothes, passing me off as a cross between a rich Russian peasant and a Biblical female in pants, lead the doorman into shy compliments and nervous glances. He thinks I'm another one soon due on stage. I quickly move away, feeling guilty at such easy deception, vain at pulling it off, and slightly disgusted by his impressionability.

Safe now, I drunkenly survey the crowd, then weave in and out, making entrancing patterns with the weird mixtures of people. But I am only here for Jim. Searching for a familiar face to get me closer to the goal, I manage to neatly collide with Ronnie. Buying Cokes to take back for the band, he acts a bit suspicious and edgy until he sees I am, as usual, stoned on something. This seems to relax him, mysteriously giving me a reason for being there.

Soon we're in a dressing room filled with Hollywood. I gratefully down enough scotch and grass to numb my awareness of the insistent, grating anxiety written on the faces around me like mirrors. I stand back to watch them watch each other and listen to the discreetly uncomfortable conversation. They are trying to place each other, looking for a breakthrough; this is a frightened party refusing to begin, and I want to hide.

But the door swings open and Jim, looking the sulky dark angel, arrives. There's a moment of total silence as everyone pauses, feeling his mood out, waiting to see if he's willing to guide.

I put on my face of stony boredom, believing this enables me to study Jim blatantly. He's aware of his role. While he talks, jokes, and pours out all his charm, Jim seems to be searching for something intangible. My face hasn't moved a muscle, nor have I spoken a word. In mid-conversation, Jim looks over at me, and winks. Very conspiratorial, like we're sharing a great secret. I half smile, not sure what I'm being let in on.

His wink coincides with a sudden, momentous rush as The Doors are hurried off to the audience. I trail behind the entourage in a nervous stupor, finally sitting down with Ronnie and Bill.

Jim isn't as loose as usual, perhaps in compensation for nearly falling off stage last night. Without that wild loss of control, he isn't as convincing. Tonight, his cries to tear down the myths and taboos sound guarded, and there are no blurred, sweet smiles passed on to the other players.

I watch the show come to an end. Soon it's all over, everyone's going home, and Jim has disappeared. Alone, I collapse into myself, suddenly purposeless and sick as I walk to my car. I am really tired of trying to make Jim Morrison fall in love with me without looking like I care. As if by pure coincidence, my acid ramblings have taken me backstage the past eleven months. I'm bored with maintaining my stance of a pretty girl gone crazy from Newport Beach.

Aside from that, I merely want to throw up and die. Instead, I sink down further in my seat, and rest my head against the steering wheel. The night is filled with a harsh droning as cars and people leave the Shrine in a steady stream. The world slowly becomes silent and empty as I gaze across the vacant parking lot and contemplate the tedious job of driving.

I hear footsteps and stifled laughter, my eyes refocus, and Jim filters filmically into my field of vision. Miraculously materialising from nowhere, he's walking alone, trying to look dignified; an impossiblity while being followed by a weaving group of giggling girls. They keep falling out of line and tugging at each other as he pretends not to notice. When he opens his car, one girl jumps in his front seat, another climbs on his lap and kisses him, and a third trades places with the first.

Watching this lunacy, I become fully awake, and grow reckless with determination. The door slams, Jim's car lurches into motion, and just as suddenly, I follow him out of the parking lot. We drive down two dark blocks at a ridiculously overcautious pace, then another car comes veering between us. I'm appalled to see it's an actual carload of more girls. I try to keep a discreet distance.

Looking in his rearview mirror, Jim picks up speed, spins around a corner, then suddenly slows and stops a few feet before the freeway entrance. Too late I see this is a terrible trap, and I'm caught. Getting out of his car, Jim strolls leisurely down the ramp and begins chatting with the carload ahead of me. He galances back at me with open amusement. It's hard to look haughty and aloof in these circumstances, though I certainly try. I study the Felix The Cat Tirestore illuminating the corner with purple, and frantically invent a story that I'm an insomniac housewife from the Valley out pricing tires. I'm not here for him; I'm not one of those girls.

Slowly, elegantly, Jim stalks back to my car. Bending over, he gives me a sarcastic, what's-your-story? look, and shakes his head as if he's caught me ruining my reputation. I glare at him and he smiles.

"Are you *following* me?" he asks, apparently finding this a tremendously sexy and clever line.

"I want to *talk* to you," I say in my most intellectual voice. I'm obviously not following the girls or pricing tires. I am in love with his soul, this is spposed to be a spiritual union, for God's sake.

"Aren't you going with Ronnie?" he asks suspiciously.

"No. We're just friends, I mean, it's platonic."

"I asked around and everyone said you were going with him," Jim counters persistently. "At least that's what he thinks."

"Well, I'm not, at all," I reassert. This is starting to seem too ordinary and stupid.

"That's different then," Jim says soothingly. "Why didn't you tell me? I'm living alone now, so why don't you come over?" He has this incredibly intimate, husky voice aimed at my ear. "I'm staying at a *motel*," he adds, practically falling into the car. He's obviously forgotten my line about wanting to talk.

"All right," I say.

"Just follow me. I can get rid of them, don't worry." Jim gives me a last unneeded seductive look, and walks back to his car, this time ignoring the carload of girls.

I watch him stride confidently away like some great conquering lion. I thought *I* was going to conquer *him*, now he's turned it backwards, and I want to start over again.

What's worse is my sense of anticlimax. I'm shocked to notice the moon hasn't dropped from the sky or the earth hasn't cracked open. His songs happen in places that feel like Egyptian deserts, on moonlit roads leading to the Nile or Eternity. I'm just following him over the Harbor Freeway to Hollywood. We are disappointing for two cosmic soul mates finally meeting in the flesh.

Not only am I still in reality, I'm involved in some cops and robbers escapade. The carload of girls is still hanging in, veering maniacally from lane to lane, chasing after Jim in bumper-to-bumper loops across the freeway. Resigned, I stay behind at a safe distance, feeling like a mother minding her precocious child. He pulls over to the side again, stops, and a girl jumps out of his car. After she climbs back in the car with her friends, the parade launches on again.

We pull off the freeway onto Santa Monica Boulevard. Red and furious, a fire engine roars, and I see Jim looking on benignly; his arm flung leisurely out the window as if he's watching the afternoon races. A few blocks later, the procession pulls off into a liquor store parking lot.

I lean my head back, close my eyes and sigh. Jim

merely purrs, "Don't fall asleep, we're almost there," as he walks past me into the store. I turn to glare meaningfully at the carload of girls. Surprisingly, their motor starts up and they disappear into the night. Jim comes out of the liquor store with his brown bag, apparently fails to notice his faithful fans have departed, and leans in at me, whispering, "It'll only be a few minutes now."

I'm not too sure I even want to do this anymore, but the voice inside me insists I must, or I'll be sorry someday. Soon I'm driving up a too steep entrance, under a bright neon arrow announcing the Alta Cienega Motel in blue and red flashes. It's typically Californian, under the delusion it's Spanish, with withering green vines climbing up and around rickety white lattices. Our footsteps echo over the concrete as we silently climb the stairs, and Jim opens the door.

ONCE INSIDE, I RETREAT INTO AWKWARD adolescence, standing mute and stupid as I stare at the bed. It's all the room is, practically. A Bed. I sit on the absolute edge, unable to remember my important reasons for being here, unable to find anything to say. I can't say I never do these things; he'll know how dumb I am right off. I can't say I'm not just another girl, I'm a future famous artist; he'll think I'm insane. My mind clamors on in noisy desperation until I realize he's the man, he should do something.

Jim is drinking beer and contemplating the dusty curtains as if nothing's happening. I feel as if I'm intruding or interrupting his thoughts. My presence in the room seems to slowly dawn on him, he finally puts his beer down, walks over to me, and places his hands lightly on my shoulders. Looking down into my face, his eyes invite me to stand up, his hands, moving down around my waist, command it. I stand up.

I wasn't exactly expecting a shot of beer in my mouth when Jim first kissed me. I almost choke, wonder if he wants it back, then manage to swallow without coming up for a loud gulp of air. Even finding this romantic, I decide he's real innovative, I'll just need a lot more beer to soothe my nerves. We regard each other steadily, and he smiles shyly. After I finish off his bottle, we start kissing again. Holding his arms tighter around me, Jim pulls me closer, lifting me up in a kind of unrushed passion. Getting more dramatic, he bends me back in a near swoon, pulling on my hair.

It would've been okay if it was my own hair being pulled, but it's a 100-percent human hair fall. Now the blonde mass is hanging limply in his hand. I wait for him to start laughing or pointing, but he doesn't. He acts as if everyone has two layers of hair; either that, or he isn't interested in minor details. He just keeps going. Grateful and assured, I throw off my blouse in a gesture of bravery, then fall back on the bed and stare up at him.

Jim is on stage again, conscious of his every movement, doing a private show, luxuriously undressing himself, pausing every few seconds so I'll get the full effect. He's beautiful to watch.

Standing above me, his eyes holding mine intently, he slowly slides the infamous black leather pants down his smooth, pale skin. Totally aware of the impact, he moves softly down beside me.

I lay there, mute and amazed. In a playful mood Jim indulges in a tug-of-war game with my clothes. Once I'm undressed, he rolls himself into a ball by my feet and begins examining my toes and ankles as if he's a five-year-old discovering the delightful marvels of human anatomy. He does know the direct route up my legs, his mood changing fluidly from child to man until he's moving slowly inside me, a sensual scientist searching and finding all the right slants and curves. Maintaining the quality of unhurried passion, he's lovely, mastering each sensation, just as I've imagined.

It's so easy, so perfect, I feel stunned, as if I'm dreaming. I'm surprised that he is what I expected and that I'm still the same person. I reassure myself that this is Jim, his body next to mine. I slip into drowsiness, but eventually rise up to consciousness again. I remember I have to call my grandmother so she won't think I'm dead somewhere if I don't return for our weekend visit.

"I have to make a phone call," I say reluctantly, my voice visibly jolting Jim back to reality.

"You'll have to go outside," Jim says.

"That's all right," I say, relieved. I can make up a better story without him listening.

"Well, you'll have to put some clothes on then," he informs me. "I mean, I don't care, but they would."

"Yeah," I say, wondering if he thinks I'm without a brain.

"It's probably cold out there, too," he continues.

"I know." I've thrown on a bizarre combination of his clothes and mine.

"Well, if you can't stay, we'll get together another time soon." He sounds wistful and hurt, but the casualness of his words stings me. I certainly have no intention of leaving, but I don't want to explain. Confused, I go outside and make a phone call; I shiver as I lie, but my story is accepted cheerfully.

"Well?" Jim's voice is slightly anxious.

"I'm staying."

"Good," he says, half draping himself over me. Allowing himself a contented sigh, Jim's breathing becomes deep, and without even the preface of a yawn, he's fallen fast asleep. I'm wide awake. I did at least want to ask a few questions about his writing. I pout for a while, but without an audience it's useless. Finally, with dawn encroaching, I let myself fall asleep.

CHAPTER 2

BREAK ON THROUGH

IN THE MORNING, WE WAKE TO THE steady, distant honking and hissing of traffic. Scared, Jim won't react to me, I stir nervously. He reaches over wordlessly, touches me, and we make love. It seems too automatic and perfunctory, and I'm mad he isn't talking, though I myself won't speak. I'm afraid it would be too forward – oh, the miraculous logic, I'm in bed with him being shy.

Jim stays silent. He picks up a book, *The Origins & History of Consciousness*, and props up our pillows. It is nonverbally understood we are now going to sit and read. At least, he is going to. My mind is too muddled to even comprehend a complete sentence. The book appears terribly complex, full of complicated diagrams, illustrated quotations, and endless annotations. I secretly just skim the captions and study the pictures, pretending we're looking at sophisticated funny pages.

A million hours later or so, Jim slams the book shut, and pulls out a piece of notebook paper. He begins to draw a circle, turns it into a kind of snake form, within which he creates a woman's head with flying hair. This accomplished, he looks up at me for acknowledgement. As we are apparently both deaf-mutes, I merely smile and nod agreeably. We're probably having some heavy metaphysical communication, and I don't know it. I do know I'm nearly bursting with energy. To avoid having a fit, I climb out of bed, quickly gathering my clothes as I go into the bathroom.

In front of the mirror, I regain my self-control. While applying my mascara, I resign myself to simply walking out, nodding goodbye, and forgetting this ever happended.

When I reappear with my loftily indignant, ready-for-the-world air, he immediately catches me off guard by blurting out, "What did you dream last night?" His tone of crucial importance reduces me to instant honesty.

I stand, foiled in mid-flight, trying to remember. The dream comes through, vaguely. I can tell it's just a segment of something pretty bad. "It was something about a fire that went out of control. It was really huge, and the hoses wouldn't work." I shut up as quickly as I began, embarrassed by the obvious symbolism.

Jim doesn't seem particularly alarmed. Half smiling, he motions me to sit down beside him in bed. He starts talking about dreams being interesting writing material, and telling me how he keeps his in notebooks. Then he turns them into poems. I feel like I've already read this somewhere, but I'm glad we're at least going to talk. It's so much more concrete than drawing pictures and using sign laguage.

I tell him how alienated I feel from most people, how most everyone seems unable to understand anything, how hopelessly boring, numbed and dead everybody seems. I conclude my morbid monologue with an adamant, "I mean, everyone just seems so mediocre!" I wait patiently for Jim to save me from this wretched dilemma. I'm sure he can, though my logic is clearly suspect. Out of pride, I've neglected to mention his songs have practically caused these problems to appear, so only he can make them disappear.

To my horror, Jim is acting as if these ideas are new to him, as if he's never noticed masses of morons in our midst. He mulls it over for quite a while. Then he agrees with me in a surprised, sorry voice. "I guess most people really are mediocre."

"Well, doesn't it even bother you or anything?" I plead, shifting impatiently.

"When I was younger, I was more idealistic. I always thought it was just a matter of time, you know, before I had a lot of friends, close friends who were doing the same thing as me. But it never happened." It looks like this just hit him. "The other guys in the band are like brothers, you know, *brothers*. But not really friends. There's a difference, you know. I mean, I like them, we work well together, but we're not really alike." Jim stops reflectively, as if burdened by an old dream.

"I'm really glad to see the hair on your legs is light," I say idiotically. "I was really afraid it might be black." I don't add I'm also glad he doesn't have skinny toothpick legs as my girlfriend sarcastically predicted. It's already bad enough that he doesn't have any friends and that he was young such a long time ago.

"Did you know my hair is really red?" Jim asks brightly, cocking his head sideways so I can really tell.

"It is not. It's dark brown." I flatly refuse to accept his statement.

"No, it's red! There are all kinds of red highlights and

streaks in it. It just *looks* brown. You could tell if we were in the sun, it's actually red."

God, I can just imagine him out in the sun, hunting for a red strand with a mirror. This really annoys me, especially because his main girlfriend, Pam, has real red hair, not his kind.

"You've really got a thing about red hair, don't you?" I ask, wanting to get up and leave.

"Well, I just think it's sort of rare." He pronounces *rare* in this slighted, defensive way, and looks at me distrustfully, as if rare things are beyond me.

"Don't you think it's weird that you're famous?"

"I just think it was a coincidence," Jim answers, as if he thinks I'm interviewing him about the success of "Light My Fire." "Something just comes along at the right time, and it *happens*. We never thought it would be a hit! You know, I wrote the music, and Robbie wrote the lyrics. Everybody always forgets that." Seeming very impressed by these facts, Jim pulls the sheets up around his neck and stares at me, waiting for a reaction.

"People get really needy-greedy looking when you get to 'We want the world and we want it now' part of 'When the Music's Over,' " I inform him. "They go all *crazy*." I sound slightly disgusted.

"Yeah, I know," he sighs, making a tired face.

"What lyrics do you like?"

"The face in the mirror won't stop, the girl in the window won't drop, a feast of friends, alive, she cried . . . " Feeling pretty stupid reciting lyrics, I stop and re-cross my legs. They're getting numb. "And the scream of the butterfly part," I add.

"Yeah, I like that. A feast of friends. I like the way that sounds . . . A Feast of Friends." Jim's sent off into a rhapsody of contemplation.

"Don't you get sick of people turning all silent and stuff just because you walk into a room?"

"Yeah, I never expected that," he sighs, a real weighted-down heavy sigh. "It even seems to affect my intimate friends," he drawls, looking at me too meaningfully for comfort.

I don't particularly want to know how this relates to me, and remain silent.

"You stood out a lot more in a crowd when your hair was real blond."

"Probably," I agree. "but I took so much acid that I just couldn't stand my hair being phony anymore. It almost made me crazy this one time. I was coming on to acid in this lavender gas-station bathroom, in one of those freeway-exit cities, you know? Anyway, after that, I had to have it dyed back to natural."

"You have to be very careful with acid," Jim says, getting real sincere looking. "It shouldn't be misused. You should just take it at the right times, when you really mean it." He sounds so reverential about the whole thing, I check to make sure he isn't making fun of me. He stays all holy looking, and I start feeling guilty about all the wrong times I've taken acid.

"I thought your performance was better the first night. You were so much looser," I say. Our conversation is so disconnected, I think we made it better as deaf-mutes.

"That's interesting, I thought so, too." He sits up straighter. "I *like* performing that way, it's better. But everyone else said it was too loose! That I was *too* loose. I don't know, that's just the way I am." Jim shrugs, hurt, like he's constantly misunderstood by countless unnamed others.

Moving closer to me, he puts his hands over my

breasts, tracing lightly through my cotton blouse. "Why did you really want to see me?" he asks, lowering his voice to utter secrecy, inspiring me with such total trust, I will admit anything.

"I've had this obsession about you. For a really long time. I always identified with you. I guess. Like you were really me."

"You mean, you think if you were a man you'd be me?" Jim is astounded by the theory he's just made up.

I'd never gone to that extreme, but maybe it's the logical conclusion.

"Well, yeah, I guess. Sort of." I'm not actually convinced.

"That's very interesting," he says, busy checking out my face.

I can't believe this incredible, amazed reaction he has to everything. I keep thinking he has to be putting me on, but he's still staring, imagining my face transformed into his. I thought he'd be more opinionated than this.

"I'm going to art school in the fall," I announce in a sudden rush of confidence, considering I haven't been accepted yet.

"Where?" He raises an eyebrow.

"Choinard."

Jim nods appreciatively, continuing to trace circles around my breast. The cloth makes odd crinkling noises beneath his fingers.

"You're very self-contained." He makes it sound like both a compliment and complaint.

"What do you mean, I'm self-contained?" It sounds like I'm a bottle of preserves.

"You're self-contained. Like you're within yourself, self-sufficient and self-confident."

"Oh. Usually people can't tell. I'm too quiet and it

doesn't show." Now I feel embarrassed and over-explained.

Jim's got his head leaned back, studying my face. I look down at my hands. He takes my hand and looks at the gold chain-link ring on my finger.

"It's a good one." He speaks gently, looking from the ring to my eyes.

I let him take the ring off my finger and put it on his. He holds out his hand, observing the effect as carefully as he had my face. He smiles unsurely, the encircling quality seems to have some meaning to him. I'm silent, feeling his mood as he slides the ring off his finger back onto mine.

"It's getting late," he says.

"I know, I have to go." I put my head against his chest for a moment, full of this pain that came unannounced. I'm bursting and suffocating with the knowledge that I can never have him – he is not something to have. Strangling, torn between the desire to ask for help or run away, I start to cry so he'll see my tears.

Jim holds me tenderly.

"I think we'll be good friends now, don't you?" he asks confidently.

"Yes."

"I don't really have many. I'm so glad this happened," he continues. "I'll be gone ten days on tour, but give me your number right now, and I'll call as soon as I'm back. Okay?"

I nod and mechanically write down my number. Quickly picking up my coat and purse, I glance into the mirror for reassurance, and head for the door, avoiding his eyes.

"Do you have your hair?" Jim asks, suddenly smirking.

"Yes it's in my purse," I say. A laugh comes up involuntarily.

"See you later," he whispers huskily.

THE PROMISE LINGERS AS I LEAVE HIM. Downstairs in the brash daylight I realize it's Christmas Eve and I never told him my name. I wonder about the man lying naked and alone in his motel room, but I can't go back. I write a note: "Jim, I didn't tell you, but my name is Judy." I put it under his windshield wipers and drive away.

CHAPTER 3

BACK DOOR MAN

I GO HOME, TO THE SAFETY ZONE, WHERE I become deluded as hell. Now that I've officially met Jim, I believe the love affair of the century has begun. The gods of truth and justice have seen my unswerving devotion; they'll take care of everything.

I float on in a blissful daze, untouched by the reproofs and arguments of well-meaning friends trying to save me; it's too late. When faith falls flat, I merely slant my vision to believe a new way.

Though the remnants of my intellect know I'm asking too much, asking for something that can never be given, that doesn't even exist, I cast that rationale to the wind. And with this reckless gesture, I'm irretrievable; I cross the line, go over the border, and wait, wait against sense, for a golden call that doesn't come.

One morning in January, I get up and dress, supposedly for school. It's awfully odd this suddenly warrants a creamy sheer silk blouse, brocade vest and mini-skirt, tinted pantyhose and my best boots.

I'm abstractly contemplating visiting Jim; I manage to maintain this vague attitude all the way from Newport to Hollywood. Reaching the corner of La Cienega and Santa Monica Boulevard, it's clear I'm not going to class. My heart makes its way into my throat, pounding wildly offbeat, making it hard to breathe, and harder to think. Dizzy, I rely on automatic control to direct me to his motel. After pulling in and turning off the engine, I am consumed with watching the shiny blue metal of his Mustang glint in the sun. I make up a story that my body's stuck to the seat as an excuse for just sitting there.

Eventually, I convince myself I'd better *do* something. I look in the mirror to remember who I am, then climb out of the car and stand purposelessly. This just makes things worse, since I'm visible, someone could see me standing there looking stricken and stupid. Walking down the sloped parking lot in a blind panic, I bump into an already irate manager.

"What do you want?" he demands.

"Nothing. I don't want anything. I just came to see someone, you know, he's just staying here."

"Who?" The man looks me up and down as if I'm an under-aged hooker or junkie or both. Flustered, I only want to flee.

"Jim Morrison."

"Mr. Morrison is not to be disturbed until three in the afternoon. He doesn't get up until then." His tone implies I'm a dubious character if I don't know these basics. "Mr. Morrison is a very busy man."

"Oh, okay, I'll just wait," I say. I slink gratefully back to the security of my car, ostensibly to wait until three, though it's not even noon.

It's true, I don't know what I'm doing. But Jim will explain it all to me. His existence justifies everything.

I begin counting the bricks using different mathematical systems, trying to calculate how many bricks I can count per minute, how many hours to count the entire wall, and how many times I'll count it before Jim comes out of his room. The wall blurs to a grey sheet before me.

A door slams, an engine revs, shiny blue metal glints in the sun, and I jolt to life. Nonchalantly falling out of my car, I walk to his. The late morning air seems moist and clean from the night's rain. Jim rolls down his window and smiles up at me. I've never seen anything so beautiful as his face, gentle in this light, calm, almost radiant. I can't speak.

"Hello, Judy." He says my name softly, amused, possessed of himself.

"Hi," I croak, about to keel over yet acting poised.

"This is a nice surprise," Jim drawls. "I'm just going over to Elektra for a little while. Do you want to come along with me?"

I look down at particles of damp black gravel caught in the deep grooves of his right front tire. My brief hesitation causes Jim to quickly reconsider.

"Oh never mind, you'd probably get bored. It'll be faster if I go alone. Will you wait for me?"

"Yeah."

"Okay, I'll hurry and be right back. Here's my room key. Don't let anyone inside but me," Jim warns, smiling, as he hands me the key. "See you soon," he promises and drives away.

HE HAS CHANGED ROOMS. THIS ONE IS larger and more lived-in. Magazines are flung open across the floor, books are falling from stacks like playing cards across the dressing table, and scraps of notebook paper are scattered all over. The epigraph, "They're All Scared," is scrawled darkly by his nightstand. This must mean me too, I guiltily surmise. I'm even afraid to read his black journal though it's inches from my hand. (It would be bad Karma or he'd catch me.) I sit gingerly on the edge of his bed, and pick up *The Tibetan Book of the Dead* in hopes of distancing reality by making it cosmic.

I've read a paragraph, and am imagining golden rose molecular light exploding as my soul leaves my body, when the maid comes in, scaring me into the corner chair.

Shaking out a pillowcase, she smiles hopefully and asks, "Are you an actress?"

"No, I'm an artist, I paint," I answer. She looks at me with some disappointment.

"Is *he* an actor?"

"No, he's mostly a singer. And he writes," I add apologetically.

I watch words swim across the page in black moiré patterns as she tears off sheets, replaces them, dusts, and changes towels in an efficient flurry. The maid leaves as quickly as she came, meeting my eyes with a timid smile that makes me sad.

I read intently, preparing to meet Jim on a high abstract level, though I've been drawn to him mindlessly as a narcissist to a mirror. Jim is youth, male beauty of a grace and delicate destructibility; he's riding this cold merciless wave of passion straight out like fire. And I have loved him for this – for living impossibly rather than dying in intolerably slow, aching, degrees. He is my glorified inner-self made public.

By the time I hear Jim's whistle approaching, I've disintegrated to a vapor, more prepared to discuss the relative degrees of death according to aura colors than kiss him. I'm a floating energy mass of white light when he knocks on the door, and I let him in. Jim immediately throws his arms around me, kisses me hard and passionately, bombarding me with his raw sexuality. My spine freezes and I feel rooted by gravity as he double-locks the door. Much as I've sought him out, I don't know how to take him.

"Oh, God, my boots are *killing* me," Jim yelps, collapsing backwards on the bed. "Please take them off," he moans, rocking forward. His eyes cracked half-open, Jim looks like a disobedient child trying not to smile as he purposely makes his legs dead weight. Quickly bored by my ineptitude with invalids, he props himself up on his elbows and helps by turning his ankles inward. Jim begins to show more cooperation when I reach his leather pants, easily arching his slight body away from the bed.

His right hand pauses lightly on the nape of my neck; he grasps my hair by the roots and slowly pulls me up beside him.

"Let me undress you now," he orders somberly, holding me back at arm's length. He ritualistically removes each piece of my clothing, folding it meticulously before moving to the next.

Once we're both naked, Jim quickly coils and strikes, sudden as a snake and I'm stunned on my back, caught watching a movie I'm acting in, and he's directing. His black-framed angel face rises above me, simultaneously innocent and corrupt, blending good and evil, god and beast, while looking down upon our bodies locking below.

As if from an insurmountable distance, I watch the demonic half of his face taking over, as Jim demands, "Tell me you want me to fuck you."

"I want you to fuck me," I mumble, sounding like I'm reading from a script I don't understand.

"Say it like you *mean* it!" he yells.

"I WANT YOU TO FUCK ME," I scream furiously.

"Good. That's good. Now tell me you love it, you love me to fuck you."

"I love you to fuck me," I murmur, reverting to my bad acress role.

"Come on. Now, tell me. You love it, you love it. *Don't you?*"

"Yes," I whisper.

"Then *tell* me."

"I love you to fuck me."

"COME ON, I said TELL ME!"

As I repeat the words reluctantly, Jim listens, his face fluctuating rapidly, changing essence until a cold, wild element tyrannizes the others. The black line curving above his upper lip grows darker, taunting, accentuating the menacing edge in his voice. "Have you ever been fucked in the ass?"

"Yes," I try to sound pleasant, but bored.

"I want to fuck you in the ass."

"I didn't really like it that much. I don't really *want* to. Don't, okay?" Too late, I know Jim's seen my fear and feels contempt.

"I *want* to," he hisses, cold with fury, hollowing me to the marrow. His eyes are black, blazing with hatred and defiance.

I'm afraid he's going to hit me, slap me, shake me, and something dies, drops out of me. Let him have my space, let him take over mine, I think, backing off in psychic terror.

Jim has pinned my arms down, flat against the bed. He looks so crazy and cruel, I realize he could kill me, and I'm sorry I didn't listen to the people who warned me. The surroundings blur, all definitions are lost, there is nothing, nothing but his incessant driving need pushing brutally over the edge, out of control, until he even forgets I'm there. I realize he's raping me.

Suddenly, I become violent, twisting beneath him, lashing out like a crazed animal for survival, clawing and screaming at him to stop. Just as suddenly, he stops.

His eyes register surprise, widen back to blue, and fill with tenderness, focusing on me as if I'm a child he loves dearly. Still holding his weight on my forearms, Jim bends over and kisses my forehead and mouth softly, sadly; a wistful longing plays across his face as he looks straight into my eyes. He gently traces my cheekbones and nose with his fingers. I stare back, bruised with incomprehension.

"I'm going to take a shower now," Jim says in a polite TV announcer voice. "Come on in, if you want."

Staring at the ceiling, I nod, and remain motionless. I soon realize he's not coming back to comfort me and waiting for an apology will only humiliate me further.

I find Jim washing his hair and whistling, in an excellent humor. He smiles shyly, tentatively, as I get in, then wordlessly picks up the soap and covers my body with white lather. He stands back so the hot water runs down my body, temporarily proving himself kind and considerate. The soap sliding smoothly between us, he kisses me sweetly, then lathers me up again, smiling childishly.

"I'm going to dry off now," he announces. "But stay inside, if you want." Stepping out, Jim casually turns off the hot water so I'm immediately attacked by a hard stream of icy water. I jump out.

"What'd you do *that* for?" I demand.

"I don't know, I just thought it might be kind of . . . exhilarating." His bright smile flickers to disappointment as I glare accusingly at him. He tosses me a clean towel and leaves the bathroom.

I'm drawn impulsively through the steam to the mirror to see if I have the same face. Wiping off the mist, I'm dismayed: not only is my hair drenched and disarrayed, but mascara is running in diluted black swirls down my face. This is the final indignity. Only after repeatedly scrubbing my face clean and combing my hair am I ready to face him again.

JIM IS SITTING BY THE WINDOW, LOOKING cool and collected in his white towel, apparently refreshed by the recent fiasco. Sighing, I collapse dramatically across the bed. Jim looks worried.

"Would you like a beer?" he asks solicitously.

"Yeah, I need something," I say, martyred.

"There's a store right around the corner. I can just walk over and get some."

Jim puts on a pair of faded corduroy pants and an old V-neck sweater, appearing quite likeable and unthreatening out of black leather or bed. He looks like just another hippie, until he walks. Casting me a timid, anxious glance before leaving, Jim gently shuts the door as if the slightest noise might shatter me. Seconds out of range, he starts whistling.

I throw on my clothes, reapply mascara, and struggle to compose my mind. I think maybe I'm real naïve, and I ought to give him another chance. Maybe he's not so strange – I've just been sheltered. Also, I refuse to believe that everyone else is right, and that he's as dangerous and destructive as they say. I still want to find out what he's *really* like.

When Jim returns, he's pleased to find me pulled

together, poised, no longer pouting or expecting an apology.

"I didn't mean to hurt you," he says, handing me a Miller.

"I know," I answer, feeling more calm as I swallow the beer. Drinking helps Jim relax, too. He begins talking in an easy, drifting way. He's relating, in a self-ironic fashion, what he apparently considers a semi-tragic story.

"You know, it's weird, a couple of months ago, I was at the Fillmore, I think, and I was singing. And I'd really gotten into it, you know, I'd forgotten about everything else — I really *meant* it." He pauses, looking to make sure I believe him so far. I nod reasuringly.

"And then something happened. For some reason, I opened my eyes. I don't usually even *see* people, but there were these people in the front row. And they were laughing at me. Like I was funny!" Jim picks up his beer, studies his hands, and looks at me quickly, baffled and hurt. "It's like they won't take me seriously, they don't *want* to. Even when I'm serious. I think they *make* me a fool."

Before I can answer, there's a knock on the door.

"Who is it?" Jim asks irritably.

"It's a secret!" This is a playfully lilting girl's voice.

"Come on — who is it?"

"It's ME!" She chirps.

"Oh, *sweetheart*," Jim croons.

"*Sapphire!*" She exclaims, delighted. "Hey, aren't you going to let me in?"

"I don't have any clothes on now. Why don't you come back later?"

"Jim, I came all the way down here, and now you aren't going to let me in?" She's so shocked, I wonder where she came down from.

"Now, Pam, sweetheart. I'm *busy*. Can't you just come back in a little while?"

"Jiimmm!" Pam cries, outraged. I have this perfect image of her big blue eyes growing wider in angry disbelief, her petite body raging, the long red hair streaming down her back. "Jim, I know there's someone in there with you. I just know it!"

Jim rolls his eyes and shrugs. He actually has the nerve to put his finger to his lips and motion me back against the wall.

"Well, anyway, like I was saying, I couldn't understand *what* those people wanted. Of course, you know those people in San Francisco. But New York's bad, too." He shakes his head.

"Jim, you're disgusting! I can't believe you're doing this again! If you don't let me in, I'm leaving!"

I feel slaughtered and at their mercy, even though I pretend it's a radio melodrama.

"I've been thinking of taking sometime off soon," Jim says to me. I can't loosen my frozen face muscles into a smile.

"Jim, listen, if you come out now, I'll roast leg of lamb for dinner. You have to come see my new apartment. Besides, I'll take you on your errands so you won't have to drive. Jim?"

"I'm sorry, honey. I just don't know what to do. See, there's this crazy girl in here. She's just lying on the bed with her legs open. What should I do?"

"Jim, this is it, I'm leaving!"

"But, Pam, sweetheart, you should understand, she's your sister. You shouldn't be mad."

"I *know* we're all in the same family, and everything, but I just want to see what she looks like."

"It's too bad we don't have a back door. That's one of the bad things about this place." Warming to his bizarre gameshow-host role, he grins, the comedian. I summon a front of aloof amusement.

"Jim, let me in! Let me see her, I want to see her!" Pam is getting desperate, pounding on the door with her fists, and screaming, "Let me see her!"

I feel like a piece of meat, waiting to be hung and inspected for flaws.

"Now, Pam, I think it would be best if you just get in your little car and drive home," Jim says.

"Jim, help me! The maid's screaming at the manager and they're coming! Jim, let me in!"

Outside, Pam's hysteria crescendos, with renewed door pounding, shrieking, broken Spanish, shattered glass, and masculine hands knocking on the door.

Forced to decisive action, Jim reaches for his jacket, hands me another beer and nods solemnly towards the bathroom door.

"Lock it," he whispers.

Grabbing my purse, I flee to safety.

"Get together, one more time," Jim starts singing. "Get together, one more time," he continues, walking out the front door.

I hear more slamming, voices locked in anger, pounding and screaming. I rest my head against the cool bathroom tiles, and close my eys.

Sounds rise and subside around me, gradually muffling into a buzzing silence. I've curled into a fetal postion on the floor with my slightly warm beer. I'm afraid to move, lest I be detected. I wait a long time. When I'm sure they're gone, I get up and walk in slow, listless circles trying to piece myself together. I notice my blood on the clean bedspread and hope it will make a nice conversation piece when they return. I'm torn between writing "I Hate You" across the walls or leaving my phone number so he can apologize. I do neither; I leave, looking for my pride.

CHAPTER 4

WHITE RABBIT

A FEW WEEKS LATER, I FIND MYSELF in a wretched little cell at the Sybil Brand Penal Institue for Women. I've been placed in the mentally disturbed department. All I can remember is watching a surreal and horrifying movie in which I played the main character. As she was going to be executed, contradictions besiege me. If it was only a movie, what am I doing here? And if it was real, why am I still alive? In the black reflector-glass, I see I've acquired a blue, bloated, lopsided face covered with angry red blotches. My wrists are sore, rawly crimson, and swollen. Every few minutes, someone flashes a light in my eyes. I'm obviously in a new reality. I begin weaving the hazy threads of past action back together . . .

My girlfriend Patty and I had driven up into the mountains, but halfway inside their ceaseless beauty, we lose our bearings. Patty decides we'd better get her boyfriend Ray, who will take us to a special place. Being under the influence of potent purple Owsley acid, I find everything agreeable. Smiling, I watch faces radiating in the cliffs, sending down their timeless love and wisdom.

Driving down the swooping mountain road, everything is fitting together, perfect, each second in time. As we speed down, Patty and I are still coming on, and each winding curve brings new laughter and pure joy in being alive and at the mercy of nature. I feel a reckless, soaring grace, and my life drops behind me, wonderfully justified: the Past. The wind is tearing multiple masks off my surface, stripping me down to a bare core of being. It feels good, really good.

Then the flying stops, we skid to the ground. We've reached a flashing red light at a railroad-crossing. Waiting there, I read the colored alphabets forming words over Patty's face as she speaks.

"Jim must be pretty strange," she says, forcing my disowned past into the present. I feel the shriek of the approaching train welling up inside me as I glance at Patty.

Reflective grey-blue eyes study me from her pale, cameo face. "I mean that one line, 'Women seem wicked when you're unwanted'?" Toying absently with the small ivory cross around her neck, Patty smiles curiously at me. "That's a pretty heavy thing for a man to say." She smoothes back her long red hair, and rolls her eyes. "And those pants he wears . . . *What's he like?*"

I don't want to remember Jim. Her voice is a cool murmur, a distant waterfall, as my mind screeches in panic. The train runs on, endless and ugly in the harsh, grating light. I stare at the translucent skin barely shielding the blue veins of my inner wrist. Vivid and strong, the pulsebeat is so nakedly vulnerable, I feel the blood rushing. The veins on my wrist *are* Jim.

"I have to go see him. Now!" I resolutely shift the car forward.

"Judy, I think you ought to wait a while first. This stuff is pretty strong," Patty reasons.

"But I have to see him!"

"At least wait until we see Ray. We really shouldn't be driving around like this. He'll know what to do." Patty's voice has assumed the firm, feminine logic of her mother, who always watches me as if I'm on the edge of a precarious borderline, about to meet everyone's worst expectations and plunge over.

"Okay, I'll wait," I say. Discontent rises and sticks in my throat.

WE'RE IN THE CITY. BRASH NEON LIGHTS glow through the congested air; though the white midday sun glares down from the ashen sky, it looks like twilight. Particles of fine, poisonous dust are settling into my pores. I want to tell Patty, but I'm afraid to say anything.

The stop-and-go light changes. People seem fanatically serious and fearful about catching the next red light. I suspect these people are very dangerous, with rigid rules of conduct, and they're quick to spot imposters. I try to mold my face into an expression of obedient complacency, but it's too elastic to control.

Luckily, we reach our goal: a parking lot by a pool hall in West Covina, where Patty can find her boyfriend. There's a beauty supply store, a pastrami-sandwich shop, a laundromat, and a poodle-grooming shop. I've spent so much time in parking lots, I reflect, I'll probably *die* in a parking lot.

"God, it's really intense out there," Patty says. "Do you mind if we just sit here awhile? I'm really not ready to see Ray yet. We probably should've stayed in the mountains, but I was afraid we needed Ray so we wouldn't get lost up there, you know?"

"Yeah," I say. "It's pretty creepy here." I'm relieved to hear the city has affected her adversely too, and start to trust her again, in a small, tentative way.

"You're not mad at me?" she asks.

"Not really." Softening, I smile, then I start giggling. "Patty, look at that woman over there, she looks like a Saint Bernard."

"Where?" She giggles in anticipation.

"In the blue car – over there."

"Judy," Patty gasps, "that's not a woman, it *is* a Saint Bernard!"

The dog is sitting behind the steering wheel, staring out like a mournful parody of the people I've just seen. This strikes me as hopelessly funny, and Patty and I collapse together in hysterics. Laughing, I feel as purified as I did in the mountains.

Now, a beautiful, luminous light breaks through the sky, cutting a path down towards us. Out of nowhere, a shining, crystal kingdom has arisen, majestically superimposed over the real world. Accompanied by a concerto of celestial music, golden beams filter down the drifts of silken wind, bathing the oil-stained pavement, dusty cars, and buildings with such softly forgiving, beauty and radiance, I start to cry. "God, everything is so *beautiful*! You're so beautiful – people are beautiful," I sob.

"I know," Patty cries.

We put our arms around each other, alternately laughing and crying because we're alive. As we hold each other, a sudden, raw awareness of mortality grips me.

"We wake up every morning, and then what do we do? Then what do we do?" I rush on urgently. "Night and day are continuous, not divided. There are no divisions! I mean, people just made up these separations, they aren't *real*! Like I'd even forgotten I was *alive*."

"What are you talking about?" Patty asks uneasily.

"Life just goes on forever, without any of our reasons or rules! We're in this forever too, we can't get out, even when we die! It's a *miracle*," I conclude, unnerved.

"You aren't making any sense, you're just stoned," Patty says. "Nobody can figure that stuff out."

"That's what I *mean* -- why does everyone pretend not to know? I have to go find Jim. Now!"

"Listen, I'll go get Ray, and he'll talk to you. Then maybe we can go listen to music, okay?"

"Okay, for a while." I decide to humor Patty: she's too worried to be reasonable. Just the idea of seeing Jim calms me down.

Soon, Ray approaches with a purposeful stride, Patty hanging on his arm.

"Hi Judy," he says, smiling, standing at my car door. He has a rugged, gentle face, beautifully carved, like the mountains. "Wouldn't you like to get out of your car?"

"No. I have to go to Hollywood. But you're beautiful." He really is.

"I thought you'd like to come with us now."

"We wake up every morning, and *then* what do we do?" I quiz him.

"We'll talk about that later. Why don't you get out of your car so we can go somewhere and sit down?"

I consider this for a few minutes, then notice some guys in reflector shades and black jackets slumped against a wall, snapping gum and staring at me.

"Who are they?" I ask nervously.

"Oh, those guys just take a lot of reds." Ray laughs. "Don't worry about them. There's nothing to be afraid of."

"I'm not afraid," I say, panicking. "I just have to go see Jim."

"There's lots of cops around here. You shouldn't drive." Ray's mellow voice has become so grimly authoritarian, I start laughing.

"What difference does *that* make?" Decisively, I turn on the ignition.

"Ray . . . Judy?" Patty murmurs, starting to cry. I feel I should let these nice, over-worried people know we're all alive and free. Since no one understands my words, I figure they'll understand my actions.

"We can do anything," I assure them, my laughter taking on an edge.

In one fast, erratic motion, I drive my car onto the sidewalk and sweep down between the laundromat and rows of parked motorcycles. At the corner of the poolhall, my steering wheel turns of its own accord, the tires swerve up and down the sidewalk, and the car lurches into a life of its own. Careening across the parking lot, it hits a vacant car, falls backward and mysteriously stalls.

I stare at the gearshift knob, choke, clutch, brake and accelerator with awed confusion. I can't remember the correct sequence to start the car, it's far too elaborate. Still, it would be easy enough to leave, my message delivered, if it weren't for the uniformed men gathered around, hissing at me.

AS I CONCENTRATE ON ESCAPING, I FEEL another force hitting me from below, driving me down from the land of light, crystal towers, love and freedom. It's a lower force stemming from fear and death. On this darker plane, we're born, not within God, but from a scornful, mass-production machine with hideously repetitive patterns, born into a cold, calculated cosmic joke.

I'm on psychic probation: I've violated consciousness

laws and questioned existence too many times. I should know better than to keep probing at secrets which bring death upon knowledge. My time is running out, soon my life will ooze away and disintegrate into the ectoplasmic mass, only to be remolded. I remember it's easier to be calm and not fight, but I am panicked.

I realize. these black and white uniformed men with guns are the official representatives of the lower force, enforcers of the Earth Laws. It's obvious that things aren't exactly subtle on this plane.

"May we have your keys, please?" one of them asks me. Stooping down to see my face, he smiles as if he's made a resonable request. He must have taken a crash course in psychology; he acts so gentle and harmless.

"Oh no, that's okay. I'm just leaving," I say politely. "I can't leave without my keys."

"I don't think you'd better leave right now," he says, in the same regretful but understanding voice. He's so clever, I bet he gets extra points for handling my type.

"It's my car, and I'm leaving."

"No, you aren't. Let's not be difficult, Judy."

I give the keys a violent twist and the engine comes to life. A huge arm reaches in, grabs the keys from the ignition, and unlocks the door.

"They're my keys," I scream, digging my nails into the arm. "You can't take them, they're *mine!*" The arm recedes, and the car goes dead once again.

"Will you get out of your car now?"

"No! You stole my keys," I fume.

"Will you please get out of the car?" A man with a hooked beak asks nastily. "We've asked you nicely, now are you going to cooperate?"

"No."

"Get out of that car. It's an *order!*"

"No!" As the awareness that it's their job to capture and kill me intensifies, the pit of my stomach tenses into steel wire, waiting to spring.

They huddle around spying on me, plotting their next move. A low, hissing noise presses in on me, black and venomous. A snake-like whip of bodies lashes around my car, and, without a word, the men draw in closer, forming a tight knot around me. They break into my car, pulling and tugging at my body. My hands grasp the steering wheel, the gearshift knob, and the seat as they slowly drag me from my car into their territory. As far as I'm concerned, this is breaking another Earth Law, and I have the right to fight back.

For a moment I'm stunned. "You took my keys," I say, attempting to clarify the situation.

"We had to," comes the gentle voice. Searching for his face, I'm pleasantly surprised to find it's young and kind. I stare hard into his eyes and he holds the stare. It passes through time and space; we're playing an absurd, meaningless game and we both know it. I hope we can laugh now, and explain this great farce to the others. The spell breaks instead.

I lunge forward with all my might, catching him off balance. I make a few yards progress before I'm seized from behind. I twist around, lashing at random faces. I kick, claw, hit and bite, managing to break away a few times, only to be grasped and tugged again. They aren't going to get me easily, I'll make that clear. But at last, they overpower me: with two on each side and one in the back, I am still fighting like a banshee, until I'm literally dragged and thrown into their car.

Once handcuffed, I become subdued and disdainful. Having been captured in such a disgusting, unfair way, I have no desire to continue life in this pathetic culture.

I'm a heroic martyr, Joan of Arc, let them put me to death, I don't care. I watch, speechless and sad, as we drive onto the muted gray freeway. The sunset is a diluted brownish-orange, forming a halo of smog above the dead sky. Taxes keep people like me in the back of police cars. I turn to the matron beside me and plead, "Where's Jim?"

"Don't start up," she snaps, glaring at me distastefully. She's angry because I interrupted her gossip session with the driver about new prisons, job positions and the police chief.

I study my hands. They are nice, long and tapered hands. They have many deep, revealing lines, beautiful, ancient and wise. I wonder if I know as much as they.

I turn around to study my face in the red reflector lights. This causes much consternation to my keeper, but the driver tells her to ignore me. I discover my face is quite beautiful too, though younger than my hands, and not as wise. Underneath I can detect a basic honesty and strength. I can't imagine why anyone would want to *kill* me.

I'm taken for an interview at a hopital. First, I'm made to sit in a wheelchair, then they wrap me up in seemingly endless white bandages. I'm a mummy in waiting. We go up a smudged and dirty elevator filled with spooky people. I wonder what this place *really* is. They wheel me into an iron-barred room where the resident psychiatrist for the law enforcers begins questioning me. I look at my driver and back-seat matron – they're dying to hear my confession.

"I'll only talk in private," I say.

"All right," he shrugs, and drives me into a sterile white room with bright lights. I can tell from his shrug he's weak willed.

"Will you please take these awful things off me now?" I ask.

"I can't," he says.

"I'm not going to do anything," I insist.

"I know," he feebly sighs, "but I can't." He's another one of those who pretend to hate what they do, but do it anyway, a servant.

"Well, can't you even loosen them?" I beg.

"Okay." He loosens them. Finished, he turns on me with a big, "*Why* did you do it?"

"Why are you doing *this*?" I demand. (Besides, I still don't even know exactly what I've done. I only know I'm being herded around like a cow, soon to be slaughtered.)

"You mean you don't have any reasons for what you've done?" he asks, horrified.

"Why, should I?"

"You don't want to talk about it then?"

"There's really nothing to talk about, is there?"

"I guess not," he sighs again, dismayed, "Are you all right?"

I want to tell him I'm completely out of my mind, but I don't have the energy. Besides, he ought to know.

He has already opened the door and is pushing me out.

"She can leave," he says to my keepers. They look disappointed.

As they cart me off, I look back at the poor man with his humble shrugs and sighs and say, "I'm sorry."

I HAVE CONCLUDED THAT I'M A POLITICAL prisoner, the kind they don't kill until they dissect the brain. I keep looking for possible means of escape because death is no longer the romatic end. They unwrap and unload me from the wheelchair and lead me hancuffed across the parking lot.

"Don't try any funny business," the matron says. I'm surprised at her foresight. Then I'm deposited into another car. Apparently they have numerous guest appearances lined up for me.

I have noticed throughout our journey the colors, textures, and odors of different human spots consistently match and reflect the kind of drama going on. I have found all the vibrations from our stops brash in color, dingy in texture, grating in sound, and repugnant in aroma.

A huge steel plate opens up into the sky. We enter and it slides back down, ominously. I'm so tired, I'm sick of this movie. I change my last name to Morrison, my age to fifteen, and say I have no home, to add a little variety to the script. This drives them berserk, asking maniacal questions about how many aliases I have. I say it's a joke. They're not amused.

After correcting their precious paper work, I'm sent to a waiting room. I have the company of a fat female walrus with too many parking tickets and a lady with thick black eyeliner, dyed orange hair, and fangs, who killed her husband by mistake. They eye me over and over, until the walrus finally says, "What are you doing here?"

"Disturbing the peace. I guess."

"You mean you don't even know what you're doing here?"

"No. I just don't fit, or something. I do weird things in parking lots." I don't want to talk anymore and roll myself into a ball on my bench.

Five hours later, the officials call my name. It's time for my make-believe bath, the first luxury of the house. I can tell these women pretend to be nurses, but have daggers in their hearts as they order me to undress. Instead of being intimidated or embarrassed, I turn it into a long, drawn-out, movie-star-undressing-for-her-nude-scene game. One of them catches on to me and spits out, "Hurry up, and get it over with! And scrub the tub when you're done." As soon as I get out of the shallow dish they call a bathtub, I'm sprayed with Lysol.

I'm given the latest style in blue prison dresses, about three sizes too big, and plastic thongs that cripple your walk while making dreadful noises. They must have special meetings on how to degrade women. I'm told I may make a phone call, which causes quite a stir because I refuse to use their telephone. I will not validate their reality in any way.

"But you have to call *someone*," a large blonde argues. "No one will know where you are!"

"That's fine, I don't either," I stare at her thick belt.

"We'll tell you the address," she persists.

"I don't want them to know, either." I think her belt is ridiculous and makes her look fat.

"But that's what friends are for. To help you." She's a real philosopher.

"I'm just fine without using the phone." I'm hardly about to tell her I can't remember phone numbers, names, or if this is just a big hoax.

"What did you do it for?" she half-whispers.

"What did I do what for?" My curiosity is killing me.

"Take LSD! It's a very dangerous drug. You could be dead, you know." She's quite well informed. I'm about to laugh to find my crime was taking acid. "Well, why did you take it?"

"Because I wanted to."

"Have you done it before?"

"At least forty times. I don't know, I lost count. It can be real interesting," I look at her and smile. "You should try it sometime."

This is enough for her to take me to the Institution Queen. "She refuses to make a phone call," the blonde reports.

The Queen looks up amazed, scrutinizes me and says, "You shouldn't be in a place like this. Why don't you call home?" Just like a guy in a bar, real original.

"Because I don't want to."

"It's not too late. You don't have to stay here." She's practically begging me. "I'm sure someone will come and get you."

"I don't want them to."

"All right then," she turns angry and cold. "Give me your hands." She takes them, rolls them in slimy blue ink, then blots them on paper.

"We're going to have to cut off your fingernails now," she tells me, getting out her scissors.

"Cut off my *fingernails*?" I wail in disbelief, "What's wrong with my fingernails?"

"It's for your own protection." Apparently she thinks I'm into clawing myself. "Besides, they're much too long to begin with." She pauses sadistically. "If you would just make a phone call, we wouldn't have to do it." I glance at her own crummy bitten-off nails.

"Go ahead. Cut them off," I demand. She's not tricking me into any phone calls.

Once this is done, I am escorted to my new home. I'm welcomed by weird chortling and threatening noises. The click of my cell door locking is final. The prisoners are singing two-in-the-morning blues songs about their men. It reminds me of Pam crying out "Sapphire!" I wish they would shut up and sleep, but evidently this place runs rampant all night.

I BEGIN PACING IN MY CELL. I HATE IT here, I want out. Why ever didn't I make a phone call? Suddenly, a bright light flashes in my face and a surly voice snarls, "Huddleston?"

"Yes. I guess," I mumble disjointedly.

"Your mother's here. You ought to be glad. Don't get cute," the voice says.

"Really?" I ask. I can't possibly imagine what my mother would be doing here. It's quite a coincidence.

"Yes, *really*. Now get out. I haven't got all night," the light holder growls.

I walk out through a maze of clothes-claiming, blue hand rolling, official paper work, clanks, words and bars. Finally, I reach the prisoner rescue room. I see my mother standing alone, looking frantic. I'm sure she thinks I've turned into one of those legendary LSD vegetable cases.

"Are you all right?" she asks.

"Look what they did to me!" I rage, waving my hands. "They chopped off all my fingernails! All of them. Look! Just because they didn't have any. And now they're shaped like squares!" I hold them up to her face so she'll get the full impact.

"What happened to your face? You look terrible."

"I know. I hope it's not permanent."

"Let's get out of here," my mom says. The prison employees are listening to our conversation. We give them a dirty look and walk out. Once in the car, my mother says, "Judy, please be careful from now on."

"I will be, I'm not going through that again."

And we drive off into the night – free, at least for the moment.

CHAPTER 5

CATCH
THE WIND

THUS BEGINS THE PERIOD OF THE GREAT Alienation . . . I am light-years away, as my pained ears hear past friends begging me to come to my senses. They're asking me to admit I've fallen in love with some lunatic rockstar who's almost made me lose my mind, too. But now I have a chance to come back, if I'll only forget him and whatever it was I thought I saw. My mind lets their words pass through; like misshapen leaves in the wind, they don't know me or what I've seen.

I only know I had come close to the basic core of life, good and evil, pain and joy, love and hate; all the countless dualities existing interdependently. It has been too much for me, I have distorted and lost it in my fear. Still, the gut-level truth I'd felt won't leave me, making my doubt of others grow, while my sight is rejected as hallucinations.

Most of my time is spent in isolation, reading William Blake, Greek drama, Dostoyevsky and comparative religion. I begin writing morbidly obsessive poems and begin new fantasy drawings. They're nice to look at, since they are trying to capture the glass castles I had seen. It appears to friends that I'm recovering.

To certify it, I even receive my acceptance letter from Choinard. Everyone is relieved. Art will be my only salvation, it's the only way I can release my theoretical insanity and have it accepted as creative sanity. . . .

Linda is the first to conclude I've recuperated. My eyes have lost their peculiar glint; my sentences have become lucid. I'm ready for a shopping spree in the city. We are going, partly, for shoes – there are no decent shoes at the beach. So we tour the streets and stores of L.A. After finding the shoes too old-fashioned, the people inhospitable, and the traffic unbearable, we decide to drop in on Bill, Jim's manager. We have always gotten along with him and, besides, we have a marijuana pill, THC, standing for God knows what. We'll give it to him.

Before going into Bill's office, which is also The Doors' office too, I make Linda circle around the block twice, to make sure Jim's car isn't there. It isn't, twice. I'm still gripped with irrational hesitation. We sit in the car as I carry on, "If I have to see Jim, I'll just *die*. I'll be so embarrassed. He'll think I'm there for *him*. I won't know what to say or do. Or anything!"

"But his car's not there, so how can he be there? I mean, we can keep checking all day if you want," Linda says. "Besides, I bet you really want him to be there, anyway."

"I *do not*. I would just *die*! You don't really think he's there, do you?"

"No. I already said no."

"Yeah, well he better not be. If he is, I'll just ignore him. I can't *stand* him anyway."

"I can't stand him," Linda imitates me. "Sure. That's

why you keep talking about why he's there or not, and
what you'll do, and . . . "

"Oh shut up," I say, bravely getting out of the car.

WE ARRIVE IN TYPICAL SLAPSTICK STYLE.
Bill is always sweet, thinking we're a comedy team. He
happens to be busy at this moment, so we sit down and
wait for him. I pick up a notebook from the table beside
me. It's a chaotic collection of Dada-esque poems, accompanied by drawings of squashed toothpaste containers,
squashed soap cans, and a lot of bananas and trashcans.
I wonder if the guy has heard too much or too little of
Andy Warhol, and put the notebook down. Bill walks in,
saying the book is for Jim, that he's always getting these
things, and people expect his opinions on them. I start
feeling sorry for Jim.

Bill jokes with us for a few minutes, then says he's got
to have a short business meeting, and asks us to wait
around. I want to stay, but I also want to leave, so I
compromise by sitting under a huge rubber plant by the
door. It is the same green color as my clothes, a perfect
match, and I think I'll blend in. Linda has befriended the
secretary of the moment, and is over in the corner
giggling with her. I still feel secure in my inconspicuous
disguise as I hear someone thudding up the stairs.

It is Ray, the organist, who perhpas recognizes me as
an old backstage remnant. He smiles, saying, "Oh, I see
we have some new scenery. I was getting tired of that
plant anyway. This is much better." I'm unnerved. He's
obviously hip to the fact I think I'm a plant.

Two more band members trudge through the door.
They don't seem to notice me. Maybe it *is* good
camouflage. I pray as I hear slow, deliberate footsteps

climbing the staircase. I know they belong to Jim. There is nowhere to run or hide. Perhaps he'll be too preoccupied to notice how the plant has a new deformed human shape. I look straight ahead, a petrified statue, as his face comes into view. The same face. The same husky, sexy voice, now saying in semi-surprised approval, "Hello . . ."

"Hi." I crack out a noise of recognition. He goes on to the business meeting. I hear their talking and Linda's continued giggling, and wonder why the hell I had to get myself in this situation.

Bill comes to walk us down to the car, since he has to leave too. Linda and I follow him down to the parking lot as he apologizes about time, and thanks us for the pill. I feel sick to be leaving without a word from Jim.

Outside, girls and men are coming and going; trucks, cars and sound equipment are all over. In the middle of this, Jim descends the staircase, taking it in with a bored look. He nonchalantly inspects a motorcycle, then walks over to me. "Can you give me a ride?" he asks. "It's just to Westwood."

"I don't know. It's not my car. My friend is driving." I remember I'm supposed to be mad at him, although I'm actually scared.

Jim turns to Linda, who is looking disgusted with my uncivilized manners. "May I have a ride to Westwood?" he asks her.

"Sure." Linda smiles warmly, making up for my icy behavior. Jim's hair has just been cut and he looks ridiculous. I'm having trouble keeping my laughter in.

"You cut your hair! What did you cut your hair for?" I blurt out. "I liked it better before, when you looked like a lion."

"I know." He has no humility about his previous lion-look. "But it was getting too long. I couldn't even wash it right. I don't trust people with my hair, but I was told this guy was good. I just wanted it trimmmed a little. Now it's too short. I don't care." He shrugs.

Jim sits in the backseat after a considerable flurry of who-should-go-where. I become tongue-tied. It seems he's changed from a lion into a demented chipmunk. I recall that *Pam* also bears a vivid likeness to a chipmunk. They must be meant for one another, after all. In no way could my face be said to have chipmunk features. What a way to find out we aren't soul mates.

"How long have you two been friends?" Jim asks, doing his extremely polite version of a refined old gentleman on an transatlantic cruiser, his voice full of the highest respect for young women.

"I can't remember," I say, looking at Linda who's busy not crashing into the curb. "I guess about four years."

"That's a pretty long time." Jim acts impressed. He looks at Linda in her rearview mirror and she turns red and confused. "You even look like sisters," he adds. It simply happens that we are both tan with blond hair and light eyes, like ten thousand other California Girls.

Then I look up and see Jim is still staring at Linda and Linda is turning even redder. "I *hate* poodles," I say, knowing Linda hates poodles too. "Just look at that. It's pathetic! All clipped and bowed and manicured."

"Are you going to live in Silverlake when you start Choinard?" Jim asks, ignoring my poodle tirade.

"I don't know yet. It's still too far away." I've never even heard of Silverlake.

"I used to know a girl who went there," he says remorsefully, as if she's dead or something.

I engage in momentary jealousy of this sadly fleeting girl. Suddenly excited, Jim's voice rises louder, and I turn around as he speaks. "You know this album we're working on now? Well, I think it's the best one we've ever done! I know everyone says that about what they're just finishing, but I *still* think it is."

"That's good. What are you going to call it?" I ask, wondering if Linda has completely lost her capacity for speech.

"I think the title will be 'Waiting for the Sun.' It's waiting for the s-u-n, not s-o-n." He wrinkles his face quizzically, seeming to find this fine point odd.

"Yeah, that makes more sense," I say, watching his worried face ease as he finds he's understood.

He directs us down a sidestreet in Westwood which seems to consist exclusively of shoe repair shops, old drugstores, and dental offices. He signals us to stop in front of one of these gray buildings. "Would you wait for me while I just run upstairs and make sure my friend is there?" he says. "Then I'll come right back down."

He has a clever way of making questions turn into statements. Linda nods. I smile.

I whisper to Linda that I wish I could sneak up and see what his "friend" is. He gives the word such mysterious significance. Linda looks at me and practically yells, "Judy, you don't have to whisper, he can't hear us." Then she smirks. "Gee. Jim Morrison was sitting in the backseat of *my car*. What do you think I should do?"

"Polish it, put a sign up, 'Do Not Touch,' and don't let anyone sit there, ever."

"Maybe I can get money," she mocks.

"Do you think he has a new breed of person in there or something?" I ask. We lapse into giggling and are verging on hysterics when he approaches.

We calm down like little soldiers, sedate as can be. But Linda mutters, "I like those pants better than the black ones." This makes my face twist with held-in laughter so I probably look retarded as Jim opens the car door. I bite my lip as he assures us his friend is home, he's not stranded.

He profusely thanks Linda for the ride, as if she's just donated him her last drop of blood. He leans over to me, half pulls me out of the car, and in his intimate-on-the-sidewalk-style, whispers, "Call me tomorrow and give me your phone number, I've got to see you again."

I can't understand the need for such an elaborate procedure when I could just write it down now. I also don't understand this whispering routine, like it's a big secret. I stare at him stupidly.

"I'll answer the phone, don't worry," he rushes on. "Just be sure and call at one-thirty, all right?"

"Okay, I will," I say.

"Don't forget!" He uses his everyday voice.

I CALL ON TIME THE NEXT DAY. "HELLO?" I hear. It's a male, but I don't want to be too presuming.

"May I talk to Jim please?" I ask, astounded by my steady voice.

"This is Jim." He sounds offended.

I'm slightly touched to see he really did answer the phone at one-thirty. He doesn't seem the telephone answer-er type.

"Oh. Good. It's Judy."

"So – you called . . . "

"Yes."

"I've been wanting to see you again for a long time," he says. "You just *disappeared*!"

Jim uses the telephone as an extended microphone,

carrying over the same caressing, liquid seduction. You become the most important, desirable person alive.

"Now what *is* your phone number?" he asks. I recite it in a trance. "What are you doing now?" he asks. I get the feeling he wishes I'm at some delightful orgy, just managing to call in between gasps.

"I'm sitting on the floor getting ready to go to the beach." I'm so boringly honest, I might as well add that I'm also crosslegged.

"That must be nice," he replies wistfully. "I'm going to Hawaii for ten days. I want to learn to surf in between performances."

I can't imagine his delicate, pale body converting into a brawny brown surfer's. I nearly gag. "Well, have a good time there," I say, beginning to wonder why I had to call since all he's doing is leaving again.

"Be a good girl while I'm gone."

"I will."

"I'll call you as soon as I'm back." This sounds a bit too familiar, yet I agree, shaken by his last unspoken promise as we hang up the phone.

CHAPTER 6

MY EYES
HAVE SEEN YOU

AROUND FIVE IN THE MORNING, THE phone rings, disrupting dawn's quiet sleep. My mother groggily calls, "Judy, it's for you." I stagger half awake into the other room and pick up the receiver.

"Hullo . . . ?"

"Hi! It's Jim!" This person sounds like a bright child answering an impossible algebra problem. I don't recognize the voice.

"Jim *who*?" I ask cynically.

"JIM!" The persistent, plaintive cry comes through. "Can't you even *remember* me?"

"Oh, yeah. I remember you," I answer. My heart starts beating wildly and I'm feeling faint.

"You don't sound very glad to hear from me."

"I am, it's just that I was asleep."

"You gave me the wrong phone number! All I got was a gas station in Culver City. What did you do *that* for?" he asks, outraged and injured, not bothering to hear my answer. "And then I had to go ask Ronnie for it, and he didn't even know what it was! So then I called information. There was only one Huddleston in Corona del Mar, so I figured it had to be you."

Jim sounds terribly proud of himself for suffering through such an ingenious ordeal. He asks again, "Why did you do this to me? Why did you give me the wrong number?"

"I didn't do it on purpose," I say. "I must've forgotten to give you the area code. You know there's a different area code down here."

"Oh," he says. "Why didn't you *tell* me then?"

"I said I must have forgotten."

"Well, then will you come up and see me?" he asks in a woebegone voice.

"When?"

"Now."

"*Now*? Well, um, where are you?"

"Hollywood," he says, like where-the-hell else. This really narrows it down.

"Yeah, well, *where* in Hollywood?" I ask impatiently. Understanding the practical aspect of the question, he names the Beverly Terrace Hotel, corner of Doheny and Melrose, suite number and floor.

"Are you going to come?"

"Yes. But I'm an hour away, you know." I'm sure he hasn't the faintest idea where Corona del Mar is.

"But will you leave right now?"

"I have to put on some clothes first."

"How long will *that* take?" he asks sarcastically.

"About five minutes, I guess."

"And then you'll leave? Are you really coming?" He's remarkably unsure of my intentions. "Promise me you're coming."

"I promise I'm coming," I repeat to my mother's

smothered laughter.

"Honest?" This is getting really incredible.

"Yes," I say.

"Please hurry!" he pleads, as if he's dying. Then he hangs up.

I begin rushing around in an aimless frenzy. My hair looks like hay colored seaweed, tangled from too much sun and ocean water; all my clothes look ugly. I put on some mascara, stick rollers in my hair, and hope I'm not too tan. Finally, I select all tawny brown, clinging clothes, and reason I'll look all right when I arrive. I say goodbye to my mother.

She shakes her head, looks up at the ceiling in mock nausea, and says, "Don't crash your car. I'm sure he can wait."

"Do you think I'm being stupid?" I ask.

"Would it make any difference? You'd do it anyway," she replies, logically summing up my stubborn senselessness. "Do what you have to do. I just wouldn't take him too seriously."

This raises my defenses, but she smiles and waves me off before I can start an argument about Jim's great integrity or something.

I drive with the dawn, racing to beat the traffic hour and work people behind me. Then, just as the San Diego Freeway meets the Harbor Freeway in a picturesque smog-town named Carson, my car dies with four drawn out chugs. I pull the rollers out of my hair, brush it, put on the boots I can't drive in, and jump onto the side of the freeway. Before I have to pose as a helpless female betrayed by her classically worthless M.G., a farmer in a red pick-up stops for me.

"I can only take you as far as the airport. Will that help?" The man has a pleasantly weathered, ageless country face, speaks in a slow, twangy drawl, and smiles encouragingly.

"Yes, thank you," I say, scrambling into the truck.

"No use rushing, we won't get there any faster," he observes, indicating the mounting deluge of traffic with an amused nod. This man is so perfectly incongruous and cheerful, I relax into peaceful silence. He doesn't even ask why I'm simply abandoning my car like a dead postal horse.

At the airport intersection, it's worse than New York in a blizzard. I have to fall into the street and nearly kill myself to make a taxi stop. The driver has spotted grey hair and a sneer-etched, skinny face. The second I ask to go to Hollywood, he turns around, brusquely surveys me, and says, "I don't want to be offensive, but do you have the money?"

"Is twenty dollars enough to get there? I mean, if you take the direct route?" I add, "Would you like to see my wallet?"

"No. It's just that you never know anymore," he mumbles, in his stodgy old cabdriver routine.

Blocking the man out of reality, I pull out my green eyeshadow and lipgloss, and finalize my appearance. In front of the hotel, I overpay my fare, hoping this will teach him not to insult young girls, and walk inside. A sophisticated watchdog-type sits behind the front desk. He stares at my breasts, then tries my eyes. I give him a bored look and walk purposefully up the stairs.

FINDING THE CORRECT ROOM NUMBER, I knock softly on the door. No response. I begin loud knocks and soft "Jim's?" Still no answer. I'm getting uptight; not only is my car stranded on a freeway, *I'm* stranded in a strange corridor, hissing at a door. I'm tired of being subtle, I yell *"Jim,"* while banging on the door. He finally appears, either half-drunk or half-asleep, and totally naked.

"Oh, you're here," Jim observes, letting me in. Rubbing his eyes and yawning, he walks around in confused circles, then stumbles off for a glass of water.

Though angry at his careless attitude, I'm distracted by his body. He has this really beautiful body, shaped like classical Greek sculpture; it's perfect, without a lot of overstated lumps and bulges. It seems like the male equal of mine, not threatening or alien.

Revived by the water, Jim saunters around, poses provocatively, then sits down on the bed. "What took you so long? It's been *hours!* I gave up hope."

"My car broke down."

"Oh, why didn't you tell me?" he asks absurdly. He pats the bed beside him. I stare at him uncertainly. Lying down seductively on his side, Jim half smiles up at me. "Aren't you taking your clothes off?"

I feel pretty silly standing there, all dressed, expecting a proclamation of love. Still, I stretch off my top as slowly as possible, prolonging the process of stripping myself bare without promises. Also, I'm not wearing a bra or anything, so there's no provocative mystery of shedding endless layers. I have only three meager items to shed before it's instant skin.

Jim doesn't seem particularly disappointed; he pulls me down next to him without hesitation. I want to rebel, but I remain silent, letting myself roll aimlessly over the bed with him. It's sort of fun, and we're frolicking around like clumsy puppies. When he kisses me, the purpose is clear, transfusing me with warmth.

"Eat me," he says in a long, sensual drawl, causing

an electric bolt of shock and excitement to shoot through me, making me strangely, totally alive. A little later, deeper into the game, Jim begins his theatrics.

"Why did you give me the wrong phone number?"

"I didn't. I told you – I forgot the area code."

"And I got a gas station. A *gas station*! You did it on purpose. You wanted me to go through this, ask other people, call all over just to get your number. Didn't you?" I look at him silently, wishing I was so devious, wishing I could've done something like that. "Then, you didn't even remember who I was!" His voice is hurt, outraged, and thrilled.

"I was asleep, it was *only* five in the morning."

"You bitch – you did it on purpose! You really are a bitch aren't you? Answer me!" I can't, I'll ruin the ruthless, wonderful castrating character he's invented for me; I'll bore him with my wholesomeness. "How many men have you fucked since me?"

"None," I say, wishing I knew something better than the truth. Appalled, I look away. I can't admit I'm too hung up on him to even *look* at other men; they're all so boring, dumb and inferior. Having too much pride to reveal this deficiency, my answer sounds unconvincing.

"*How many?*" he demands again. "I won't get mad, I just want to know."

"None," I repeat, forcing myself to meet his eyes. He's looking at me with open derision and disbelief. I feel both relieved and disappointed, then have an impulse to laugh, and bite my lip.

"You're lying." Jim watches my face in fascination. "Aren't you?"

"No. Really, it's the truth. No one," I say, feeling my eyes flickering ridiculously. It's so funny that he won't believe the truth, I have to look down and think of something sad so my eyes will stop laughing.

"Are you making fun of me?" he asks, now convinced I'm a genuine liar, wicked as hell. I shake my head, distrusting speech. "You're a bitch and a whore, a bitch and a whore!" I'm too amazed and shy to protest. "You're a *whore*, and you love it!" Jim adds, gleefully hateful. I guess my new role is one of daily crucifying men in some decadent way.

Just as I'm beginning to adapt to this concept, he changes moods, becoming airy and flowing, so we're making love on a light, goal-less pleasure ride. I'm relieved, I don't have to think anymore.

The early morning sun comes softly through the French windows, gently illuminating us. Insulated from the outside world, we move slowly in front of the gilded mirror, lost in mutual narcissism.

At first we're lovely, our striking contrasts mold together in warm, rich patches of light as in a pre-Raphaelite painting. I'm tawny brown with masses of golden-red hair falling over his translucent white skin. Soft black waves frame Jim's pale face, his light blue, all-seeing eyes shoot steadily through the mirror, pinning me there, locking us in time.

"We're animals fucking," Jim says moving behind me. "You're an animal." As I become aware of an ethereal, female quality emanating from his dark frailty, I find something fearfully alive, almost predatory in my own carnality. "We're wild dogs, fucking," Jim insists, holding me there.

I'm frightened by my own fiery vitality, the wildly voluptuous presence that threatens to take over the mirror, and overpower us. I'm relieved when we tumble back on the bed.

"Remember that time I fucked you in the ass?" He

gives it a sweet lilt, like reflecting on a walk in the summer rain.

"Yes." I would've forgotten it if I could.

"Don't you want to do it again?" he asks moving slow and soft.

"I told you I didn't like it the *first time*!"

"But I'll be very gentle," he pleads.

"No! I don't want to!"

The door opens then quickly closes. This causes Jim to go berserk, losing whatever control of himself he originally had in an erratic climax. I'm pleased in some vehemently illogical way.

"It was the maid," Jim says. He fixes his pillow so he can lean on it sideways and stare at me. "I didn't feel like coming, you know. I just wanted to enjoy it. And then *she* walked in and it caught me unprepared. I wasn't expecting that!" He thinks this over as if it's terribly complex. "I wonder why it affected me that way?" His eyes fill with wonder and a child's wild hope that I can explain his behavior.

"I don't know," I answer. I don't know why he does anything, but I have gathered analyzing his behavior once it's over is one of his pet hobbies.

"You know I don't *really* think you're a whore, don't you?"

"Yes."

"You mean you understand?" he sounds fairly elated.

"I think so," I say gloomily. I think it's that he wants to believe I'm as fickle and free as he, and if I'm a liar and a cheat then he doesn't have to worry about hurting me. I certainly can't let him know I'm faithful and honest, and worse, believe if I go along with him, he'll eventually fall in love with me, too.

He's cheerful as he stands up, explaining he has to

make business calls. He places his hand on my head, gently rubbing it as he dials. When he speaks, Jim uses his intimate public voice, still sexy and husky, but more refined, gracious, and deepened in authority.

"Hey, listen, this is serious. My hotel bill better be paid right away, or they might throw me out on the street! And they won't take anyone's check."

Placing one hand over the receiver, Jim puts his other hand under my chin, lifting my face up so he can see it better. Looking at me in total astonishment, he says, "You're beautiful."

I smile, thinking it's about time he noticed. Now perhaps he'll finally notice I happen to be an unusual human being, too.

"Right now I've got to meet everyone downtown for some passport pictures and some other hassles. It'll be hot and smoggy, but you can rest here. I won't be gone more than a couple hours at the most. Won't you stay?"

"Yes," I say. I'm certainly in no hurry with my car lost somewhere on the freeway.

"Good, then we can make love some more. You'll really be here when I come back?"

"Yes," I say, giving him a small smile.

"See you soon then," Jim says speculatively, and locks me in his room.

RELIEVED TO BE ALONE, I FEEL DEVIOUS enough to look in the drawers. Karma lashes up at me in the form of a note on U-Haul paper. It says: "Jim, I'm off for England. Hurry over. I love you. Pam." I stare at her words and handwriting for about three minutes before I slam the drawer shut in nausea. I walk wearily into the bathroom, deciding a good hot shower will cure me.

Stepping inside the stall, I close my eyes and stand like a supplicant, hoping the hot water cascading over my body will restore me. Through a filter of steam, I watch drops of water form on the creamy ivory tiles, fall together, and slide down in glistening trails. Leaning against the cool, wet wall, I see a blood-stained bikini bottom lying on the turquoise blue tiles. This is almost more sickening than Pam's note. Watching the rivulets of water eddy down the silver drain, I wonder where the owner left her top.

Wrapped in a turkish towel, I quickly leave the bathroom, turn on the '68 Democratic Convention, and walk around the room, letting the air dry me off. My eyes fall upon a pair of abandoned pantyhose hanging forlornly on the window ledge. The toes are gently draped over the stiff, silk back of a lemon brocade chair. This is just about too much evidence for me to digest. I throw my towel to the floor, fall back across the bed, and start to cry.

"I dwelt in the palace of loose exile, playing strange games with the girls of the island," keeps whirling, mercilessly through my head. I'm not some dumb island girl to play with, I think, pulling the covers over my head. Once it's impossible to breathe, I decide Jim must have a reason for doing these things. I throw the covers off and come out of hiding.

I am greeted by my mirrored image. I look so fresh and healthy, I can't imagine why he isn't madly in love with me. With long bangs and my hair turned redder from the sun, I even have some of the chipmunk look of Pam. Just from some angles though – my cheek bones are too high, and my nose isn't short enough. Still, I feel confident all over again, brush my hair, and turn up the TV. They're saying all sorts of fascinating things at the political convention. I'm feeling fine when I hear Jim's whistling coming down the hall. For someone who is supposed to be so *tragic*, he sure whistles a lot. Then he opens the door and smiles, like he's just come home.

CHAPTER 7

SEASON OF THE WITCH

JIM IS HAPPY, FULL OF ANIMATED TALK about the great Japanese restaurant they found downtown. The entire trip turned into an adventure when he'd expected an awful pain.

"Oh, I shouldn't be talking about food, you're probably hungry. Are you? We can eat somewhere if you are," he says.

"No, I'm not at all, really." This is true. Food sounds repulsive.

"Have you been bored?" he asks, assured at least that I'm not hungry.

"Actually, it's been nice doing nothing for a change. It's kind of relaxing."

"Yeah, it is good for you," Jim agrees, laying down beside me, and smiling sweetly. He sighs, rolling his head across the pillow to look up at me shyly, almost worshipfully. His eyes are wide and vulnerable, full of a child's Do-you-like-me? look. When he takes his defenses away like that, with so much hope and trust, it takes my heart and mind away. All I want to do is reassure him, love him; he's an aberrant stray with no mother, lost in the world.

We both feel so young, so new and tender, hugging each other for all the love in the world never found. We're holding each other with the warmth and strength of those, then, forever friends.

Near tears, Jim sobs, "If it wasn't for this, life wouldn't be worthwhile."

I can't answer, I can only keep holding him. The desolation in his words scares me. I'm not ready to face the sadness and defeat in his voice.

Jim changes over again, like a sudden desert storm. He wants to make love and starts throwing off his clothes as if it's the last day on earth and this is our last chance to make a stab at living. His wild desperation mounts. He cries, "Now, now, now," over and over again. I know he justs wants to feel the moment, but it starts sounding like he's on stage, and I wish he'd find some new material.

"What are you?" he asks.

"I don't know," I look at him in confusion. "A girl?"

"No. You're a cunt," he says slowly, in the patient, uninflected tones of a teacher speaking to a possibly gifted student. His pupils dilate, forming a black core that penetrates me. I can feel his violence prickling under my skin, threatening to erupt between us. "Now, what are you?"

"A cunt."

"Whose cunt?"

"Mine, my own," I blunder defiantly.

"No! You're mine. You're *my* cunt." He gives me a desperate, searching look, his voice is raw and anxious. "Do you understand that – you're only mine, *I own you*."

He scrutinizes me, waiting for resistance. I give none,

feeling strangely secure and comforted, under the delusion we're locked together in some primeval way. His
harshness subsides.

"Now, what are you?"

"A cunt."

"Whose? Say it."

"I'm yours. I'm your cunt."

Later, laying peacefully beside me, Jim asks, "Do you
know what I mean when I talk to you like that?"

"I think so." I feel he's trying to define sexuality, in
a sadly clumsy, egocentric way. He looks at me, steadily,
determining if I really know what he means.

"It's hard to explain," he begins.

I shake my head, not wanting to hear his explanation;
I like my imagination better and don't want to be
disappointed.

"No. I *do* know what you mean," I say.

Relieved, Jim curls up content and docile as a cat in
its favorite spot.

"You know," he says, an astonished, happy look
spreading across his face. "We really get along well, don't
you think? We should really spend a lot more time
together. It's so easy to be with you!"

"It's easy to be with you, too," I smile, thinking he's
awfully slow to catch on. We both stare at each other,
embarrassed.

"How old are you now?"

"Seventeen."

"You're pretty young," Jim says.

"I'll be eighteen soon. My birthday's in August," I
answer defensively.

"You take birth-control pills or something, don't you?
I mean, if we're going to keep seeing each other, we don't
want you getting knocked up or anything."

"I grew up on them," I answer icily. I haven't heard *that* expression since I first had the intelligence to start taking pills. I wonder just how many girls he has "knocked up."

"I'm hungry now," I announce.

"Uh, there's a problem. I forgot, but there's a friend coming to meet me for dinner. I guess we can all go together." He looks confused. "I'm afraid all three of us would be awkward?"

Besides his ability to turn questions into statements, he's also quite deft at making statements questions.

"I don't see why it has to be *awkward*. I'm starving to death and sick of being inside."

"I guess you're right, after all." Jim smiles, easily convinced. "Let's get dressed now, so we won't be late. I'm always late!"

WHEN WE GO OUTSIDE, THE SMOG CONTENT in L.A.'s air has produced a twilight mirage of colors. The evening light is incandescent lavender, pink and salmon. Standing under some palms between the hibiscus and oleander, Jim's friend is only vaguely illuminated.

"You look like you're in hiding," Jim jokes.

"Shouldn't I be?" laughs a guy with a beard and an intelligent face.

When we are introduced, he acts quite personable, forgetting and remembering my name twice on the way to his car. By the time he's gone through his I remember faces, not names routine, I'm too embarrassed to admit I didn't catch his name either.

Piled into his tiny convertible, we drive down Sunset Boulevard. The night is pleasantly warm, the lights are pretty and the wind feels good in my hair. I just catch vague drifts of their conversation.

"I don't like to talk shop but . . . " Jim says, and begins talking about how much some record's grossing.

Then his friend talks about some great new equipment that's expensive but he'd like to use on his next film. Jim keeps giving me weird looks, I guess because I'm not talking.

"The lights are pretty," I say.

"I know, see *this* is why I like the city. It's *good neon*."

We'd had a debate over the good and bad points of L.A., and I'd taken the side that it was too flashy. He looks pleased to have proven his "good neon" point, without even trying.

We end up in a small Hungarian restaurant named Drossi's. I like the red checked tablecloths and intimate atmosphere. My role has changed to that of a lady, as Jim apologizes about the too-warm wine and tries to bring me out to show his friend.

"I hear you're quite a drinker," he suddenly smirks; no way to bring out a lady.

"I used to drink a lot," I say. I'm flushing crimson, hoping he's not referring to the time I got drunk backstage after consuming ridiculous amounts of vodka, Ripple Wine and scotch. Jim kept giving me scotch while whispering, "I know you're hip" and "See you later" when Pam wasn't looking.

I see a gypsy card-reader in the corner, and say, "Once I had my handwriting analyzed on Olvera street and they told me I was going to be a veterinarian when I grew up."

"Really? Do you even like animals?" the film maker asks.

"Well, I like them, but I paint." Then I notice the awful paintings hanging on the walls. "Not *this* kind of painting."

"I guess you won't even be painting animals then," he says.

He tells a story of his disillusioning meeting with Herbert Marcuse, who was wearing a stupid button. I haven't the slightest idea what Marcuse has to do with gypsies, but apparently he possesses a bright, influential mind, even if he's an inhospitable creep in person.

Though I'm laughing and acting normal, I feel disconnected. Jim presses my knee under the table, and I meet his indefinably sad gaze.

"You know, I've always wanted to do a really good death scene." The waiter arrives with dinner, and begins serving. "I would be in a meadow under some trees," Jim continues. "And there'll be blood on the white flowers falling over my face."

"The Beef Stroganoff," the waiter says, clearly un-amused.

"Oh. Excuse me," Jim chokes in mock horror. "You shouldn't talk about Death at the dinner table."

The waiter leaves haughtily, I discreetly gulp some wine, and Jim collapses into adolescent laughter. Non-plussed, the bearded man launches into a tirade on film and theatre criticism.

In the middle of enjoying my Beef Stroganoff, I look up and say, "I'm eating meat. I wish vegetarians weren't so didactic or I'd probably stop eating it. I just keep eating it on purpose, it makes me so mad!"

"I think it's a new form of religion." Jim sounds simultaneously amused and respectful, looking up for approval.

I don't know what to say, I'm so busy feeling guilty about eating slaughtered animals.

Jim talks about his coming trip to Europe, especially England. He wants to meet the Beatles, but he's afraid they've never heard of him, or, if they have, they'll reject him.

"But they always have tea, all the time, for everyone, don't they?" asks the film maker, who then answers himself, "Yes, it's a custom, at three in the afternoon or something."

"What if they just laughed at me?" Jim asks.

"I think you should just *do* it," I say, tired of such a fuss.

Jim looks offended by my easy solution. He turns to the subject of Mick Jagger, whom he saw backstage but didn't speak with. I guess this proves English Rockstars hate him or something.

"Jagger looked like he'd been through a lot of hard times but had come out all right." It sounds like one of his silly statements to the press. I wish there was more warm wine.

The film maker says it will be interesting to see how "Hair" is done in L.A. after leaving New York. Then he says we'd better leave or we'll be late. I don't know where we're going, they haven't told me. On the way there, Jim turns charming and tells a story.

"When I was young, my mother used to watch Art Linkletter on TV everyday. She really was hung-up on him. One day, he said he was a passionate collector of those baseball cards that came with bubble-gum, you know? So, my mother, she *believes* him; she went out and bought all this gum, and mailed him all the cards! I don't know *what* she thought would happen." He begins laughing. "Then a few weeks later, Art told the audience he'd been putting them on. My mother was heartbroken. That's when I decided I'd have to be in the entertainment business."

I can't tell if this is something he's just invented or if

it's really true. It's funny in any case, and the air is filled with laughter. We pull up in front of the Huntington Hartford Theater, shining brightly with a big crowd outside.

With no warning, Jim leaps out of the car, saying, "I'll buy the tickets now, so we don't have to stand in line."

As we park the car, the film maker is still laughing. "Jim's really funny," he says.

"Yeah, I have a headache, though." I rub my temples.

"Oh, I'm sorry. I don't have any aspirin." He sounds sympathetic, and he has nice brown eyes.

"If I just concentrate on not thinking, it will go away." This is my secret way to get rid of a headache.

"You can *never* stop thinking!" he protests.

This dogmatic statement infuriates me, I stop rubbing my temples and am about to tell him about semantics when Jim comes back to the car. He's exhilarated and full of ironic comments about people in crowds. He hands us tickets as if each has secret meaning. The night looks jewel-lit all down Vine. He leads us through the people, and we enter the theatre.

The play's called "Do Your Thing." I watch people cavorting about on stage, spouting their happy, free lines, being androgynous, and doing their thing. I begin to hope it's really satire. Jim's main concern during the second act is that one of the leads has her zipper open. He keeps mumbling how he feels backwards and uncomfortable *in* an audience. Maybe he ought to go pull her fly up, or at least tell someone. But he doesn't, saying perhaps it's intentional.

When the day ends, I'm relieved to find they're also disappointed. Jim doesn't hold my hand or put his arm around me; he doesn't even jab me in the ribs. I pick apart my appearance piece-by-piece looking for a reason why he won't touch me. By the time we're in the car, heading for another unknown destination, I'm positively sulking. I just want to be in bed with him, even if he is crazy.

A few minutes later, we're sitting in the Los Feliz movie theater watching French shorts about adolescence and sex. They're good, at least they're real. The main feature flashes by as a series of images. There's a mangled war and some sick soldiers take over a small country family. A gun is held up a woman's skirt, and they behave in a revolting fashion to prove whatever they can't prove.

Jim leaves for a Coke, and on returning growls at me, "Fancy meeting you here. Haven't we met before?"

Then an anarchist Joan of Arc-type woman is shot down like a deer in the woods because she won't break for the men. I identify with her until she's dead. The ending has the same macho soldiers back home showing off picture-postcards of Athens, Rome and Paris, as they brag of their conquests in the midst of their terrifying impotence.

I think this movie's pretty good, but it depresses the hell out of me. I don't even want to talk anymore, especially now that the night has become almost scandalously beautiful with a full moon shrouded by clouds. Jim and his friend talk on, oblivious of me, when to my surprise, the film maker turns to me and asks my opinion on the post-card scene.

I'm glad he knows I'm intelligent and wants to show Jim, who has the nerve to remark, "Oh, she's fallen asleep already."

"I have *not!*" I say. "I found it alternately fascinating and boring – back and forth."

"That *is* a problem Godard has with repetition," the film maker agrees. "Sometimes he pushes it too far. It's a very tricky technique to use right." He and Jim lapse back into this conversation on film devices. I contemplate suicide as an alternate technique, a bloody, wordless one on the corner of Highland and Sunset. I figure I'll just end up with a broken arm or something.

At the hotel, Jim's friend, evidently having forgotten our headache-and-thinking dispute, asks, "Would you like a ride anywhere?" He must have observed the great non-rapport Jim and I share.

I'm surrounded by silence, and Jim pulls a poker face. I know I should leave before things go from bad to worse.

"No. Thanks, anyway," I say.

Jim and I get out of the car.

MY BOOTS ARE TOO NOISY. THEY SQUEAK horribly as we silently climb the stairs.

Inside his room I finally admit the truth. "I don't know where my car is. I left it on a freeway somewhere. I just *left* it there!"

"I do things like that, too. Sometimes you just feel like that." He pauses. "Shouldn't you call someone and tell them where you are?"

"I guess so," I answer begrudgingly.

"Feel free to call anywhere you want. The phone's right there." He motions in case I'm blind and goes off to the bathroom.

"Hi, I'm not dead in case you were wondering," I say to my mother, hoping she'll understand my fake frivolity.

She does, and begins a series of what's happening-what's-he-doing questions. I come up with a lot of cryptic sentences, letting her know I'm okay but the situation's bad. As soon as I've hung up, Jim comes out, toothbrush still in his hand, and stares at me.

"You must be awfully close to your mother to talk to

her like that."

"Yeah."

Jim has the audacity to actually put on a ridiculous pair of boxer shorts, as if he has to protect himself from me. He slides into his side of bed. I keep sitting there, fully clothed, wondering what to do. My car's stranded, it's late, I lost the ride I should've taken, and I'm too embarrassed to call friends.

"Well, what are you doing?" Jim finally asks.

"Thinking."

"Are you getting in bed, or what?"

"I guess so," I really can't think of anything else to do.

I undress, making sure my bikini underwear shields me, too. He'd better know I'm not in the least interested in him. I crawl to the far right side of the bed, so near the edge I'm about to fall on the floor. I turn over on my side with a belligerent movement and glare at the dark wall. I'm not here, it's all a hallucination on his part, the dumb bastard.

"Have you ever had a boyfriend?" I could never have dreamed up a worse insult.

"One and a half," I reply sarcastically. Then to my horror, I go on to explain my answer honestly. "I mean, I've had a lot of minor boyfriends, but only one and a half major ones."

"Oh, it's just all impossible," Jim says in a stunned, tragic voice. "It never works out, something's always wrong. You believe all these things about love, but it's never true the way you thought. Still, you keep believing something will work, and it's just not *possible*! Never."

"What about Pam?" I ask, cast into the role of a sharer of love's hopelessness. I'd always thought she was the main thing keeping me from him. I wish he'd just come out and stab me with his devotion to her.

"Pam?" he questions the name vaguely. "Oh, I don't know – she doesn't really understand me. We've been together off and on for a few years. It's not *really* anything. I love her and everything, but it's just never what I want. I don't know. I guess I'm just not ready. I just don't want to be alone."

Jim drifts off sleepily, leaving me as unsure as he is. We fall asleep miles away, separated by an arm's length.

A few hours later the phone rings, and Jim reaches over me to answer it. It's Pam, calling from England. She's forgotten time is different across the ocean. I'm shocked to hear how angry and curt he sounds.

"Don't you realize it's the middle of the night here? It's after three in the morning! Call back when I'm awake," he orders, slamming the phone down.

After a spell of plagued sleep and the nightmarish semi-consciousness of being unwanted, the phone rings again. It's morning now, and Jim is nicer.

"Hello, honey," he says, the easy familiarity jolting me with pain.

Fully awake, I grab my clothes and get out of his bed. I dress hurriedly in the attached sitting room, then sit and listen to their inane conversation. They're talking about which airline has the best food and whether or not she's old enough to gamble.

It takes Jim quite a while to realize I've permanently moved into this other room. By the time he finds me, I'm smoldering.

"Would you like cab fare home?" he asks.

"No." I'm not being paid for anything.

"Well, would you like a ride anywhere? I can't drive, so the secretary's picking me up. She could drop you off somewhere."

"No, thank you."

"It's not any trouble!" Jim keeps up his reasonable attitude. I'm not in the least interested in being reasonable. "Well, what are you going to *do*, then?" he persists.

"I'll think of something," I say.

He sighs. It's clear I don't know what I'm doing or what I want.

Jim takes a shower, brushes his teeth, and dresses. When he's done, he comes back and gives me a long, exasperated look, as if I'm beyond belief and he's not.

"Okay, I'll take a ride to Bel Air," I finally condescend. He nods, pretending to be amiable. It's hard not to trip him as we walk downstairs.

Climbing into the car he can't even drive, Jim introduces me to the secretary-driver.

"This is Judy. She needs a ride to Bel Air." His tone makes me sound like a lunatic guest star.

The girl smiles at me, then quickly turns up the radio full blast. Jim taps his hand on the car roof, in time to the music, apparently thinking it's a wonderful morning.

Turning around to me, he over-politely asks, "Which girlfriend are you going to visit?"

"He isn't a girlfriend. I'm going to a boyfriend's. His parents are in Europe." This ends all attempts at further communication. I speak only to the secretary.

When we start driving up Stone Canyon, part of me relaxes; I feel comfortably enclosed in the long winding tunnel of familiar green trees.

"You can pull in here," I finally say, relieved.

I get out of the car and thank the girl for the ride. Full of sudden confusion, I look at Jim, unable to decide if I should scream I hate you or I love you. I wish we could just be friends for a minute, but he's not looking at all receptive.

"See you later," I say stiffly. He gives a me a frozen smile, and I walk up the front steps.

CHAPTER 8

STRANGE DAYS

STANDING ON BOB'S STEPS, HOLDING MY hand up, about to knock, I manage to recognize that the shouts "Judy, Judy!" are coming from another direction. My name is being called from the pool area, along with gleeful splashing and laughter. I walk through the side gate and up the grassy knoll, besieged by happy, tan, and stoned wet people, all greeting me as if it's my surprise birthday party. Some are friends from the past, others strangers from the present.

It would be embarrassing to launch into a love-has-ruined-me scene, so I say vaguely, "My car is lost on a freeway somewhere and I have to call Linda to pick me up."

Everyone seems to think this quite a grand situation, Linda will add to the sunny reunion. Bob ushers me off to the guest house for a bathing suit and telephone.

As we walk, I mutter under my breath, "That was Jim, who just dropped me off and left me here. He can't even drive his own car."

"So that was Jim just leaving my driveway?"

"He was rotten, absolutely rotten to me. He doesn't have feelings. Besides that, he's weird."

"You love it," Bob laughs.

"I do not."

"Well, anyone who sings about angels . . . " Bob gives me a look that says I knew damn well what I was getting into and that it's pretty dumb to act hurt when you're intentionally playing with fire. "Come on, forget it, change your clothes and call Linda."

Moments later I am floating luxuriously on a soft raft in the lagoon-type pool, my fingers trailing whimsical patterns in the blue-green water. I'm hit with the total incongruity of life. Here I am, dawdling in the water on a beautiful summer day, surrounded by lush, varicolored foliage, rose gardens and pretty people, and my heart is nothing but a stone pit. Watching my fingers tracing swirls, making liquid paths, I see that after a few mirroring undulations nothing is left, the pattern is gone. I take this as physical proof that nothing lasts; things live only for the moment, to die without a mark, and disappear forever.

This is difficult to come to grips with in the middle of a swimming pool, especially around old friends who at least expect some confirmation that I am, indeed, the same old crazy Judy who will do anything. I finally say I'm very tired, haven't slept and am in a mood. The attention shifts away from me, to the dog who is retrieving balls in the pool.

Linda arrives, cheerful as hell too, already in her bathing suit, merrily chiding me for my behavior, but careful not to ask me questions once she sees my face. She joins in the fun I assume to be going on. I hear her planning a reunion with Bob and Sam which will include me. We four are the original take-acid-in-the-garden-and-revel cohorts.

By the time we leave Bel Air, it's set that we'll all be getting toether next week at the beach. I agree, we'll have a good time.

BOB AND SAM ARRIVE ON SCHEDULE, thoroughly equipped with miraculous orange LSD mixed with STP. They say it's exclusively for Linda and me. Bob informs us, as an authority, that it will be "an unforgettable experience."

I'm not particularly interested in unforgettable experiences since my encounter with the uniformed men. This assures Bob I have all the more reason to take it and get a fresh perspective. Linda feels it's all getting passé; she's sick of walls breathing purple paisleys and seeing trails for days. We finally look at each other, simultaneously shrugging our shoulders, in mutual what-the-hell moods.

After swallowing my oversized pill and concluding it has no effect on me, I walk down to the beach alone. The sunset is blazing red, orange, and magenta, misting over the ocean with its diamond glimmer. The beach is familiar and I feel at home, barefoot, digging my heels and toes into the just cooling sand. As the knot in my stomach gets tighter, I grow more engrossed with the silver veins of water riveting tiny canyons through the sand. Rainbows flow in liquid obedience out to sea, swallowed, and incorporated into the enormous, blue curls.

Focusing on the gentle waves leaving saltline kisses on the sand, I see wet brown strips and bulbs of seaweed thrust out of the engulfing whirls. I crack the glistening bulbs open, watching stored bits of water trickle out and filter back to the sea. This plant seems more an animal with its body extended out into long, myriad arms, clutching the sand. It will soon be dry, dead and discarded if it doesn't let go and fall back into the tide.

This makes me uneasy. I edgily notice it has become dark and turn away to walk up the craggy path which brings me to the top of the hill. Light dust particles stir around my feet, and I pause a moment in awe at the supreme stillness.

When I go back into the house, I have a knot in my stomach. Linda does, too. Bob hadn't mentioned any lasting stomach knots in the deal.

"Just wait a little while," he assures us. "Or you could just take some more."

This is said as a joke, but Linda and I think it's the obvious solution.

"Remember this wasn't my idea," he says.

I'M GAZING THROUGH THE WINDOW, ONTO the peace of evening and lovely twisted vines, when some moron blasts out the entire room with Jim's maniacal screaming. "Waiting for the Sun" has been put on the stereo. I'm extremely annoyed with this indelicacy to my mind. I was having a pleasant time forgetting, now his soul is richocheting off the walls.

Jim is carrying on his desperate dissertation of the Unknown Soldier to an absurdly frantic point. The military killers are lined up, one-two-three, huff, puff, power-madness, the robots of death, setting up the unknown soldier – and wham, he's blasted dead, visions of blood and gore splashing, the militia's victorious retreat with the church bells ringing. Jim is singing, "It's all over, all over, all over."

Linda walks across the room, her eyes berserk. "Let's get out of here!" she says.

We escape into the bathroom, shutting out all the noise. We take off our clothes and get into the shower, turning it on full blast, so the hot water will soothe us, save us. Showers are safe, sane and soapy. After a while, we're much better, only a little stoned, perhaps. We're new and clean and there are no wars. When our fingers start wrinkling to water-logged proportions, we get out. Wrapping ourselves up in furry towels, we sit down on the tile floor to invent nonsense and laugh some more.

There's an exaggeratedly polite knock on the door and Sam whispers, "Are you accepting visitors?"

Sam is a dear old maniac, and we let him in to listen to our curled-up cosmic gossip. He laughs with us, and presents me with my just-washed and -dried jeans. I'm informed I got them sopping wet and dirty while reveling in the seaweed. This is hysterical since I can't remember being wet. It's resolved we're blithering idiots in need of a good meal; we put our clothes back on.

In the kitchen, Bob and Sam play aimlessly with the spices while they pretend to make food. We're introduced as the Shower Girls to three guys; one of them owns the stereo, the records and the house. They are, collectively, members of a band with Sam in San Francisco. I'm sick of bands and stare at Bob in consternation.

"You're a mirror of *everything*. I just have to look in your face to get a reflection," Bob says.

I walk out of the room to stare at myself in a real mirror. Bob is deluded; I have a perfectly distinct face, not some mass conglomeration of others. I was also deluded to think I was hungry.

We troop into a bedroom and shut the door. The music tries to sneak in as the door closes. Spared of such an imposition, we sprawl across the bed to make fun of the world and ourselves.

I feel secure, wrapped in delighted mockery with these friends, when strangers walk in. A piece of Jim Morrison comes blasting through at me. I clam up in horror. Everyone else is quiet too.

"Say something *scornful*, Judy," Bob urges; he loves my indignant act.

Now I've forgotten it. I'm confused and off-guard, inanely mumbling, "Hair and cloth, woven images."

"That's very sensual sounding," Linda encourages.

But that's it. Sensual images, strangers and Jim. I click over instantaneously.

"Where are my keys?" I demand distrustfully. "Who has my *keys*?" No one answers.

Silence takes a malignant reign. I'm in terror now, the earth-enforcers are after me *again*, still trying to kill me for some damn rule I keep breaking.

Knowing the house has already been invaded, I jump off the bed, then run out the nearest door into the street. Noises echo after me, but they fade. I think I've evaded Them, especially as they weren't particularly bright, just very brutal.

Finding myself alone and quiet but for my panting, I'm somewhat relieved. I'm sitting on a ledge of earth overlooking the ocean.

"Are you all right?" a timid voice asks me. I turn to find I'm not alone; Linda is sitting next to me.

"No," I burst out, "I'm scared!"

"What is it? Those people? I mean you just suddenly *ran away*." She puts her arms around me because I'm crying.

"It's just that I've seen too much too fast. I know all these things I'm not supposed to know yet. I think I'm going to be punished for it. I mean, I think I'm going to die for knowing," I confess.

"You know you aren't literally going to die." Linda looks scared, but her voice is calmly mystical. "When Nick got into meditation too fast, without supervision, this happened to him. I mean what you're talking about is just what he used to be afraid of. He was real susceptible to things like you, too. So, he just had to slow down for a while." I wonder if he had things chasing him, too; maybe this is an everyday occurrence.

"Besides," Lynda continues rationally, "We've got this *drug* in our systems, that's what's causing everything. We just have to wait for it to wear off."

"Don't leave me." I plead, only semi-comforted.

"I won't. Don't worry," she says. "You know, we could go to a hospital. They would just give us something to come down."

"Oh, no! No, I'll be fine. I don't want to do *that* again."

White sterility images flash at me, and at that instant, I notice the light on the night horizon watching me. It's a judging Cosmic Eye, in league with the Earth law enforcers. This eye has witnessed my confession to Linda, which is proof I had better be disposed of before I can create worse havoc on the planet.

I'm appalled at the thought of staying under the control of these inevitable forces forever, never to escape the cycles, not even in death, which is an invention. I see time is also just another reassuring invention we made up – it obviously does not exist, there's just this multi-layered somethingness. Everything has happened before, it's all repetition, variation on a theme; we've been all people, we're everything.

I can't say this aloud to Linda, or I'll be immediately zapped away – the powers that be will ascribe it to some organic death like a heart attack. I begin acting composed, calmly saying I feel much better. I suggest we return to the house, where I think I'll be less vulnerable.

I find everything profoundly symbolic, even the shadow under a lampshade. Panicked, I walk down a hall, and find it covered with green paintings, lush forests that tremble, beckoning, waiting for my entrance into them. Of course, I'm too smart for such a ploy; I'm not getting trapped there for eternity.

At the end of the forest-trap hall, I find a bedroom and walk inside. I lay down on this waiting-room bed, surrendering to fate. I hope my voluntary cooperation may win me some kind of pardon. It probably gets tiring chasing and capturing all the stray disobedient souls flaunting themselves recklessly across the continents. They'll show up sooner or later. I might as well be ready and waiting.

I look up and see the framed face of Jesus on the wall. I've never really identified with Him, but I can see He's here to save me by the expression in His eyes. He seems to be forgiving of people like me, which is consoling. Whenever I hear threatening sounds outside the room, I look up at Him for reassurance that they won't get me.

I wait a long time, but nothing else happens. I just keep looking out the window at the vines weaving themselves together in unperturbed, nocturnal plant life. Suddenly, I hear a loud clock ticking beside my bed. It must mean there's time again since it wasn't ticking before. All the timeless forces have missed their chance to abduct me. They've lost their power now, like the full moon leaving the werewolf a mere person. My eyes fall down on a Cinderella book planted on the floor. I let out an involuntary sound, it's a sick laugh. It's more than ironic to wake to Cinderella and the clock, in semi-reality again.

When I walk out, I'm besieged with questions. I say

I'm fine, fine, and I've never heard of this Jim Morrison person. He lives in a book, with all the other creatures of fantasy. I feel very, very old, unable to answer more stupid questions.

Linda talks with the others about what should be done with me; they agree I should be taken home. I just follow directions, getting in Linda's car and staring bleakly at the half-dark greyness called dawn.

ONCE HOME, I FIND OUT I SHOULDN'T BE there. I'm in a pyschotic condition, and my mother is there. She's subjected to watching me illustrate my deep, nonverbal thoughts by drawing trails across the air. Swirling senselessly with magical twists of my arms, hands and body, I'm Isadora Duncan beyond reason. She watches long enough to determine I'm harmless, then leaves me alone to come down.

This is fine with me, I'm sick of being watched like some sideshow freak. I dance around a while longer, then go over to my dog. He's been watching me, but in a mild, nonjudgmental way. Sitting down on the couch together, we put our heads under the drawn curtains, and look out the window. This is the first truly intelligent creature I've run across all night. We nuzzle each other in full understanding, then quietly watch the new light filtering golden rays into the garden. The deep green of the plants is dewy and the flowers are opening to the day. It's good to have this calm, accepting being to help me see in such an appreciative way. I only wish I could be so aware and loving.

After the sunlight has turned the world to morning, I arise from my trance and see a magazine called *Time*. This is a pretty comic name, and in the corner I see the words "August 1968." That's apparently the present, though it sounds like years ago. Leafing through the pages gives me the courage to understand my paranoia.

To begin with, I was born and raised in California, where nothing lasts and everything is new. There are no carved pillars. We believe in progress, when evolution is just a word for surface change; we believe God is dead, when God is a word for what's beyond and between birth and death, for forces within and without, everything and nothing. Everything and nothing is all that's left to believe in. My mind echoes as I walk to my bedroom and collapse in sleepless exhaustion. It's the last time I ever take LSD.

CHAPTER 9

MY BACK PAGES

IN THE FALL, I BEGIN TOURING LOS AN-
geles in search of a place to live while I'm attending art
shcool. I have the basic fantasy down – it will be high in
the hills, secluded by green trees, made of wood and
stone, with a good fireplace. Here, Jim and I will unite
as the unparalleled lovers of our time; he will come over
for candlelight dinners while we plan our future. This will
consist of my graduating in four years to achieve artistic
acclaim as he continues his poet-entertainer thing. Then
we'll be married and live together as blissful geniuses. We
will travel sometimes, but mostly I'll paint and be famous
in a field not competitive with his. He, already having
money, will of course, pay the rent and whatever else has
to be paid.

I somehow managed to get straight D's in homemaking. I suppose this was gracious on the part of my
teachers; it would've been embarrassing to explain how
one could *fail* homemaking (although all I could do was
make burnt hot chocolate and lopsided gym-bags). When

our class had its climactic test on the Home Arts, I blew it. It was a make-believe formal dinner, for which we each invited a guy as a surrogate husband. In the middle of this somber occasion, I spit my milk all over the table in a fit of hysterical laughter. The ideal hostess would *not* conduct herself this way. I had to leave the room. My only saving grace was being the "Dramatic Type." I could soar around in black capes and if I was lucky, some unsuspecting fool of a man would propose before my looks burnt-out along with my brains.

My behavior might've been better tolerated if I hadn't shown equal contempt for everything, except for an occasional English, Drama, or Art class. Teachers were always secretly calling me aside, saying they'd looked up my I.Q. tests, I was extremely intelligent, so why did I get such lousy grades? Caught offguard by this flattery and disapproval, I'd go blank and say I didn't know. Maybe if I were paid higher prices for A's, I would go to U.S.C. and marry a doctor, too. Civics was such a bore, I sniffed cleaning fluid to stay awake. This was probably unfortunate, as it was a chance to see how the politics of money and power worked, and note that only men played the game. Evidently, the women were making dinner, sewing, and having children. I wasn't going to be equipped to do either.

Now in Los Angeles, with the sobering rents, I can understand my teachers' concern.

THE FIRST DAY AT CHOINARD, I MEET A girl. Because of her last name, she is standing in front of me in line, and I lightly kick her leg to get her spaced-out attention. I have some question about registration. She turns around, her large eyes looking shocked. I'm pretty shocked myself to see a girl in a short skirt, wearing a bra under her blouse, and carrying an efficient looking bag. I wonder if she's a secretary who got lost. She answers my question, surveying me through her light freckles and long dark hair. After striking up a conversation on the eyewracking psychedelic walls, and the psychotic acting girl in the front of the line, we reveal our common plight. She has already come to the conclusion that it would be financially easier to live with a roommate than alone.

Later, she informs me I looked like a confused California combination hippie-surfer-cowgirl. She looked like a lost secretary. But she has a great excuse: She just spent nine months recuperating from flipping out in Europe; she thought a normal disguise would make her normal inside.

Neither of us want to live near Choinard, which is located next to MacArthur Park. Driving by is enough. It is full of wrecked-up people, shabbily glued to peeling benches, staring at street gutters full of muddy papers. The entire area is a bummer for Buddha first leaving the palace; all the aged, alcoholic, sick and crazed are discarded and forgotten here. It's a bit much to swallow, and impossible to justify.

We manage to find a small house in Laurel Canyon that fits what we want. It even half-fits my original fantasy. It seems as though everything is fine, until the day I bring my first carload of boxed possessions, mostly books. Walking up the steps, I find myself blocked by the landlord's body. He's standing a few feet above me, oblivious to the weight of my balanced boxes. As a matter of fact, he's irate. His face is beet red and he's making all sorts of weird, threatening noises, and inexplicable, frenzied gestures. I back off accordingly.

"Your check bounced! Get away – I won't have liars and cheats living in my house! There's no telling what else you'll do."

As he gestures, I wonder if he's going to fall down and have a heart attack. His face is changing colors, moving from red to magenta, and becoming purple. It's disconcerting next to his snow-white hair.

"Get out. Can't you hear me?"

"Well, I don't see *how* it could have bounced," I finally speak up, baffled.

"It did. It was a bad check! You gave me a bad check, you can't fool me! I called the bank!"

"But, it's impossible, there has to be a mistake. What good would it do to give you a bad check?" I ask.

"You girls are just bad! I should have known. You have no respect! How can you just stand there and lie like that? Oh, I'm glad I found this out before you moved in. Now get out!"

This is so amazing, I start to cry, a stupid move, but every time I try to speak I lapse back into tears.

"Phony! You aren't going to get anywhere with me using phony tears! Don't think I haven't seen your kind before!"

"I am not a *phony*," I say, suddenly cold with fury. This man has obviously had a rotten love life, it's no wonder he doesn't trust a soul. "Also, I would never even *bother* to write you a bad check, and if you can't understand that, I . . . " I start crying again, my point lost as I look down at all my homeless boxes.

"Leave me alone!" he motions wildly. "Get away from here now!"

I pick up my heavy boxes, give him my most polished glare, then turn and walk away. He's still screaming at my evil back as I get into the car; while driving away I see his arms continuing their frenetic waving.

After I turn the corner, I'm overcome with a siege of hysterical tears, based on the utter cruelty and injustice of the world. Driving down and around the Laurel Canyon curves, boxed in traffic hour madness, I'm suddenly convinced I will see Jim.

IT ISN'T HARD TO COME ACROSS HIM. He's walking alone, down a sidestreet near his recording studio. Yet I'm in no mood for reflecting on my intuitive powers, remarkable as they may seem, I rarely remember to use them. I pull the car over while calling, "Jim!" out the window.

He looks mildly astonished, but he recovers with expert skill. Getting into the car, he says, "Hi, Judy, how are you?" as if it's just been three days, not three months, since we've last seen each other.

"Horrible," I sniff. "This horrible thing just happened to me!"

"I'm sorry I acted so cold to you," Jim continues, oblivious to anything else. "But you were beginning to act too possessive."

Me, acting possessive? He was acting like an iceberg or worse.

"If I'd had any sense I would've just gotten mad and left!" This doesn't seem to make much of an impression on him.

"Do you want to go somewhere for a drink?" Jim asks.

"No. Something *awful* just happened to me." Actually, I'd love a drink but I'm afraid to go to a bar because I'm only eighteen. It would be too embarrassing to get hassled, though I never have been before. Jim is sitting there sodden as hell: He wanted a drink. I launch into my story. I end with a melodramatic, "I'm just so sick of everything, won't you hold me?"

He makes a half-hearted attempt but it's awkward with all the damn boxes.

Jim has cheered up considerably. He finds all kinds of psychological vantage points and brings the problem into simple focus for me. It boils down to something resembling a reverse Electra Complex.

"Has Kathy ever lived away from home?" he asks, not waiting for my answer. "Her father probably doesn't want to lose her, you know, so he wrote the bad check, so he could keep her."

"No." This is ridiculously over-Freudian. It also implies Kathy and I are babies just released from the crib. "It's *not* that! It's that her father has two banks, and he used the check from the wrong bank, it wasn't covered in time."

"I don't mean he'd do it consciously!" Jim says. "He'd just *do* it," he says with an air of all-knowing authority.

Moving the boxes away, he wants to kiss and hold me, sufficiently touched to fatherhood by my pathetic plight. I feel rebellious and resistant, but my chemical attraction to him takes over my anger. Jim becomes passionate, past anything resembling paternal concern. He's lodged my hand firmly between his legs, while he's busy trying to unzip my pants. Really, I think, he's impossible; you can't make it in a small car full of boxes. It isn't even dark out. I pull away before he gets us into trouble. He could easily convince me of the inner logic behind getting on the sidewalk.

"You know, you've always been good to me, in bed." Jim says. "I want to keep seeing you, but it can't be all the time, you know. I mean, I can't *go* with you or anything. That's just the way I am. I'm not dependable,

I can't be a boyfriend. It would just be a few nights together, every few weeks or so. Would you do that? I mean, could you handle it? That way? I don't want you to get hurt."

I figure since I'm already hurt, I don't have anything to lose. Also, I feel like he's challenging me, asking if I can "handle it." I say that's just fine. He acts pleased with my casual, mature attitude towards his hopeless character.

"Well, just think about it a while tonight. Then call me tomorrow and give me your new number," he says.

"That's really a nice outfit you're wearing," he tells me. I wonder if it's a joke, but see he's serious. "You really have good taste in clothes."

I suppress my desire to giggle. I intentionally picked out the straightest outfit I owned, in order to impress the landlord. Now, instead, it's impressing Jim. It seems pretty ironic, maybe he'd even get along with my father. They both like blue suede vests, crepe bouses, and herringbone pants. Jim's acting really bashful and weird, evidently having good taste in straight clothes is some amazing feminine art.

"Thanks," I manage. "I guess I'd better go now. I'm already late for dinner."

"Yeah, I'm supposed to be back recording," Jim says.

He gets out of his slouched positon. I brush my hair back into place. Then he reaches over to ruin it again, kissing me teasingly.

"Don't forget to call," he says, getting out of the car.

I begin composing a mental outline of the way to handle this situation without getting more heartache. The solution is based primarily on not expecting anything. At home, when I go to the extent of writing it down with point a and point b, I know I'll never follow it. I'm too excessive, compulsive and uncool.

That night, I have a dream in which I win Jim over with sex, and we have to explain it to Pam.

The next day I dutifully call him during my lunch break. Someone answers.

"Is Jim there?" I ask.

"Yes, but he's busy rehearsing downstairs."

"Oh. Is Bill there?"

"This is Bill." He sounds suspicious.

"Bill – it's Judy!" I say, expecting applause.

"Judy . . . Judy who?" He sounds even more suspicious.

"Judy. You know, *Judy* from Linda and Judy?"

"Oh. Judy. There are so many weird people calling here, asking for Jim, I never know. How are you?"

"Pretty good. Except I'm supposed to give Jim my new phone number. Do you want to take it?"

"Sure. I'm going downstairs now anyway, and I'll give it to him."

We talk a little more; I haven't told him about Jim and me, but evidently he already knows.

After we say goodbye, I feel frustrated. I know I'll have moved again by the time Jim decides to call. But, I argue with myself, anything's worth a try.

CHAPTER 10

GET IT
WHILE YOU CAN

THE NEXT WEEK, KATHY AND I FIND another place to live. It's in West Hollywood, what I associate as Jim-land. Neither really an apartment, nor a house, it's the other half of a designer lamp store for Beverly Hills ladies. Next door is an old rambling house where a beautiful old woman and her million-year-old German shepherd live. Although she is shy and reclusive, she leaves fresh nutbread on our doorstep.

There's a ceaseless supply of lovely men driving around. I remark to Kathy that at least it makes a nice background.

"Yeah, and they're *all* gay," she adds.

"Oh, come on. They can't all be gay!" I protest.

"Yes, all of them. Or practically all of them."

"How do you know?"

"I can just *tell*." She looks at me like I'm remarkably naïve. Kathy is particularly adept at spotting gay men.

Our street corner turns out to be a major meeting place and I find the barely disguised pick-up procedures fascinating. Walking along abstractedly, men gaze into interior decorating shops, look at the sky, or talk to their dogs. Then, ever so accidentally, there are two instead of one in front of the same store window. It seems so civil, and sophisticated in comparison to the "Hey baby, where ya goin'?" approach of most heterosexuals. But by the second night, I'm bored enough to use earplugs to block out the courtship noises.

Driving home from Choinard one afternoon, I'm compelled to ask Kathy to take the alternate La Cienega route. I've become irrationally nervous, to the point of wringing my hands like a soap opera heroine. I am positive Jim is going to appear any minute, and anxiously tell Kathy. To my amazement she makes a face, and says, "I know."

Two blocks later, we see him crossing the street, wearing a straw Mexican hat and a beard. Kathy's mouth falls open when I jump out of the car.

Heedless of the honking traffic, I run across La Cinega and emerge on the sidewalk, panting and wild-eyed.

Jim has watched from the safety of the curb, apparently not finding my reckless appearance unusual. He looks me up and down and smiles serenely.

"Want to go for a walk?" he asks, not missing a beat.

"Where?"

"Around the block. I've got some time. Why don't you give me your new address before I forget." Flourishing his black notebook and a pen, he takes down my new numbers.

We walk to the corner and turn down a quiet side street as dusk settles in the neighborhood. The first autumn leaves stir in the light breeze and crunch beneath our feet. I feel as if we've been transplanted into a small, midwestern town. Jim's face is molded softly into a rare peaceful expression as we circle back to the boulevard. We hesitate, but the noise intrudes further, interrupting the mood; red and green lights flash like chaotic warning signals from the curb.

A woman and her blond daughter wave avidly and approach us. They're carrying souvenirs from Jim's record company.

"Oh, you're Jim!" the mother exclaims, with the triumphant exaltation of a tour guide. "May we have your autograph? We both just love your songs!" She continues, smiling as her bashful adolescent daughter blushes prettily and stares at the ground.

"Why, thank you. Do you have any favorites?" Jim asks, absently stroking the darkening stubble on his cheeks.

"Oh, 'The Crystal Ship,' " the young mother says enthusiastically. "Are you growing a beard?"

"Uh, let's just say that I'm trying it out." Jim shrugs for the make believe-camera. He's not just polite, but disgustingly charming, transforming into an official superstar. "I may shave it off tomorrow," he confesses.

"Oh no, please don't!" she begs, enlisting her speechless daughter for help. Pretty and pained, the daughter nods agreement.

I begin to retreat. I try some deep breathing exercises while I slink off to lean against a building and look bored. I begin to feel I'm watching a foreign language film with occasional, jarring blasts of English. As they walk away, charmed to tears, I fight back a desire to tell them he's a maniac.

"They seemed nice," I say, noncommitally.

"Weren't they?" he sighs, enthralled.

"The girl was really pretty."

"The girl? Oh, no – I liked the *mother!*" He looks wistfully back over his shoulder.

We're walking down a back alley, propelled aimlessly by his state of bliss and my disorientation.

"Come here – look!" he says, motioning towards a strange, abandoned building. "It looks like it's just been *deserted*!" Excited, he sticks his head through the door. "Wouldn't this be a perfect place to fuck? Now, just all of a sudden?"

"Maybe . . . "

Jim slips inside, quickly swallowed by the darkness. Blindly seduced by the eerie emptiness and the unknown transient feeling, I follow.

"There's even a bed!" he says. "See?"

All I can make out is an amorphous black heap in the center of the room. I venture to the edge of the dark shape and touch it.

"This is fiberglass!" I cry, running my fingers over it. "I'm allergic to it. I used to get rashes on my stomach from laying on fiberglass boats. It hurts!"

"Then you can just get on your knees and I'll fuck you from behind!" Jim says, throwing his jacket down. "This is for your knees, okay?"

"Yeah, but be careful," I say. I add some of my own clothes and climb onto the heap with mixed feelings.

"Jim," I lament when I can stand, "there's fiberglass just *embedded* in my legs, and they're all itchy!"

"Good, now you'll have something to constantly remind you of me."

Jim strides across the room, finds a bare shelf in the corner, and starts writing in his notebook. I straighten my clothes, brush my hair, and wait. Jim keeps writing. I open and close my purse, take out my keys and begin jangling them. He shifts his weight back and forth like James Dean. I get up and walk over to where he's standing.

"You get so nervous sometimes, you make me nervous too," he complains.

"If you'd just let me *talk* about being nervous, then it would just go away," I say.

Staring at each other in silence, we simultaneously move closer, Jim inclines his head sideways to kiss me; a fraction of an inch before my lips, he stops.

"We'll both be in Hollywood for a long time. We have plenty of time."

This statement is his reason for stopping a kiss that was already feeling like a culmination of something indefinable.

"That's true," I say, and we walk outside.

It is sunny and beautiful, the sky is a stunning azure blue, full of miraculous white clouds. Feeling light and expansive, I turn to Jim, making a sweeping gesture upwards.

"It's *beautiful!*" I exclaim, bursting with inexplicable energy.

Jim looks at the sky, then at the building and me, and says, "This will be our place."

I wonder about that, but an illogical happiness fills me and I feel a contagious smile spreading across my face. First Jim looks puzzled, then a helplessly awestruck expression comes teeming over to me. He is a shy kid with a timid crush on a girl, and it's all beyond him. I love his face, the way it gives his soul away, so unabashed and pure.

Aware of my temporary power, I give him a careless, happy smile, and say "see you" in a vague, promising voice. Letting myself be blown freely, I turn down the alley away from him. I float home in a rhapsody; it takes all my concentration not to drift into cars.

When I reach home, Kathy wants to go shopping. To

her amazement I agree, and we leave for new print bedspreads, curtains, candles and flowers.

THE NEXT DAY I'M HANDED A MESSAGE in my painting class that says: "Call your mother, urgent." I ask Kathy to come with me to the phone booth because I don't want to be alone when I find out what's so urgent.

My mother lives in a large house in Laguna with her friend. Bev answers the phone, saying my mother can't talk now. Bev fumbles around, then blurts out, "I don't know how to tell you this, but your dog is dead."

I can't understand her. This is my sweet dog, my loving-eyed friend. Words flow out of the black plastic object in my hand.

"It was over in a minute, he was just hit on the side of his head. A little gash, it hardly showed – his body wasn't hurt. He died instantly."

I throw the vicious black object causing this pain at the air, so it will go away.

Kathy catches the phone in mid-air, she begins a factual, unemotional conversation with my mother. (I can talk to my mother's friend, my friend can talk to my mother, but we can't talk to each other. Telephone death etiquette.)

I'm crying too noisily for the halls of Choinard, so I run away to hide in my car. A perpetual wave of disbelief and tears keeps welling up and over: *not* that little brown dog, that shy and free creature, so loving, understanding, and so damn trusting. *He* hasn't been killed by some cold mute machine. No.

Alone in a parked car on a listless and empty street of downtown Los Angeles, silence overtakes me. I gaze at the shreds of student's old drawings, feelings and insights made into art that are thrown out or lost, beckoning from chipped sidewalks and gutters. I feel the great empty space widen, wedging us all in – each single, glorious and irreplaceable as the tiny purple flowers hidden behind the fences nearby. Eternity yawns and widens for each leaf on every tree, it widens farther and swallows us.

CHAPTER 11

PIECE OF
MY HEART

THE NEXT NIGHT, I COME UP FROM A disturbed sleep, thinking there's a maniac outside my window, winding a gigantic surreal clock. Time passes away, making that long, constant clicking sound. Frightened, I open my eyes, but the sound rapidly diminishes. The clock by my bed says it's just after two. Kathy is staying with her boyfriend, so I'm alone for the night. There's a knock on the door and I leap out of bed. Wondering if I should arm myself with a kitchen knife, I tiptoe to the peep-hole. It's Jim.

My fear turns to irritation as I swing the door half-open. He looks sheepish, half smiling at me.

"Can I stay with you?" he asks in his unloved, orphan voice.

I glance past him to the limousine in the street, its engine purring as it waits for him. Maybe *that* was the clock sound, I think. I stare back at Jim's expectant face.

"Okay," I answer slowly.

Appearing mildly drunk, he lopes out to the car,

motioning for it to leave. I walk back to sit on my bed and
wait for him. He comes stumbling in, mumbling "no
lights" as he falls mournfully across me and my bed. I
gather he's suffering from another bout of life's mistreat-
ments.

"Weren't you even going to invite me in?" Jim moans
after a few moments of silent agony.

"I don't know. I was having a dream about this clock.
I didn't know it was you."

"You didn't exactly act glad to see me. It doesn't
sound like you missed me, either," he says, his head
resting on my lap.

I'm in no utopia myself, and I shift impatiently, tired
of his having a corner on hell.

"My dog was run over and killed yesterday afternoon," I announce. "Also, my legs have a rash all over
them from that fiberglass!"

I actually have this theory that if I hadn't been with
Jim at four-thirty, my dog wouldn't have been run over
at the exact same time, but it sounds too farfetched to say.
Jim pulls out of his collapsed position and regards me
with renewed interest. Knowing I'm suffering seems to
perk him up.

"I bet you never expected life could be this hard," he
says, stroking my head affectionately. "You're still so
young," he adds compassionately, his face yearning and
heartbroken.

To my surprise, I break into sobs and Jim wraps me
in his arms, gently protective.

"Come on, let's pull the sheets back and get in bed,"
he suggests. "There's nothing else you can do."

Lulled by his tender authority, believing in his voice
and the implicit promise that he can make everything
right again, I obey him.

It feels so poignant, two intimate strangers wrapped around each other in a twin bed. The gentle side of Jim is strong now, but I can tell he's about to break into tears himself. I want to ignore this. All I want is comfort, not sex, but he pleads with me to leave the past behind. I feel so lustlessly earthbound, unable to brush off my troubles.

"Come on, Judy, let it go. Come on!" Jim's voice is hoarse, pleading brokenly. "Let's fuck death away, now, fuck death away!"

His frantic despair seems to reverberate off the walls, surpassing any need of my own, building out of control until he's dying with his last anguished calls. Soon he surrenders his chaos for peace. Relieved, I sink back against the pillows.

We talk softly, sadly, about nothing, really. Jim is anxious to hear my impressions of life, as if listening to my fresh exposure will give him new clues to existence. He's full of simple questions I can never answer, though I try. "What's it like for you now, living in the city?"

"It seems sort of bitter," I answer. "No, not bitter, bittersweet."

Jim agrees life isn't very easy. Holding on to me, he's quiet and soothing; he gives me the secure, protected feeling I need, and we both float off into sleep. When we wake up, daylight seems too brash and glaring, too sudden. Jim has been nice to sleep with, close and warm, but now he's drifted so far away it frightens me. Immobile, he's staring at the ceiling in hard, incommunicative silence. Worried, I look at the ceiling, too – some poor fool sprayed it with silver glitter flakes, under the illusion the tinsel resembled sparkly stars.

"That ceiling is horrible," I say, my words piercing the silence.

He doesn't respond. Under his scrutiny, the ceiling is

so grotesque and exaggerated, I hate it. Jim won't even talk, his eyes are stony walls of blank refusal. I'm petrified of asking him what's wrong.

I get out of bed so I won't scream or suffocate. Oddly, this jolts Jim back to life. He smiles amiably.

"May I take a shower?" he asks politely, looking mildly dazed.

As he showers, I dress, make the bed, and prepare myself for Laguna and the reality of my dead dog.

Jim comes out of the shower fresh and happy. "It's so clean and pleasant here!" he says. "May I have something to drink?

I make him a big mug of Nestle's Quik.

Jim says greedily drinking it down, "This is the best thing I've had in ages!" He's actually sincere; I can't adjust to how amazingly simple he can be.

As quickly as this thought passes through my mind, he swoops back down into depression. "I guess I'll have to call a taxi. Can I use the phone?" he asks forlornly.

I can't tell if he's feeling shy and hinting that he needs a ride, or if he want to take a taxi so he'll feel independent.

"I can drop you off somewhere if you want. I've got to go anyway," I say.

"Really?" Jim gratefully accepts this remarkable offer. "It's only Westwood. It's right on the way to the freeway, too."

Then he makes a phone call in his business voice, telling whoever it is, he'll be there soon and "it will have to be worked out."

It's the first time I've left this apartment for a weekend so I'm afraid it'll blow up if I forget something.

Standing in the middle of the front room, I say, "Let's see, now what am I supposed to do? Have I forgotten anything?"

"Make sure the water's off and the heat's off and the gas's off," Jim advises me.

AS I DRIVE THROUGH BEVERLY HILLS, JIM throws his head out the window, exuberantly waving and yelling, "Hello, little girl!" to a small blond child. She stares back insolently, refusing to acknowledge his greeting. "Snotty kid," he mutters, as if everyone should be happy that it's a damp, fresh, blue skied morning.

I'm busy pulling a floppy felt Garbo hat off and on, looking in the mirror at different angles and trying to decide if I look dumb or not. Jim watches with no comment.

"I wonder where we'll be ten years from now?" he asks.

"I don't really want to know," I answer nervously, throwing the hat in the back of the car.

"Oh, you'll probably be married and painting on the side." He says this as if I have an easy, reassuring fate.

Apparently he isn't aware that I'm not just another quaint chick artist on her way to placid domesticity.

"Oh yes." I assume the voice of the image he's evoked. "When I'm not feeding one of my screaming babies, or diapering them, I cook and I paint *flower pots!*" I glare at him, but he just gives me a concerned glance.

"You'll probably be married, too!" I hiss.

"Yeah, I probably will be," Jim sighs in resignation. He simply doesn't react to hostility properly.

Since he's more or less admitted he'll probably succumb to marriage, I temporarily forgive him for his crass comment about my art. I just wonder *who* he thinks he'll marry.

"Can I turn on the radio for a minute?" he asks,

already flicking from station to station. "I have this addiction to see whether or not they're playing our music. They're always fucking you over, so I'm always checking."

He doesn't find his current single, not that he gives it much of a chance, and clicks the radio off.

"I'll have to give you a copy of my book. It's really good, and I'll sign it for you. Then, someday when I'm dead, you'll have money 'cause it'll be a collector's item." I roll my eyes at him. "I'm serious, it will be!"

"Oh, I believe you." I mimic his deathly serious tone. Jim smiles, proud of himself.

"I think what you need is a boyfriend," he says, studying my driving.

I nearly crash at this insult. I can't believe how uncouth he is, and can't imagine what the hell to say to counter him.

"Well, I liked this one guy. But he was too stupid for me." I'm thinking of an artist I dated who ruined his image when he forgot what hieroglyphics were.

"Oh, you were just too smart for his games, huh?" He chortles merrily, but I can't figure out what he means. I think people are all pretty equal game players, and remain silent.

"You can't look for it, then it'll *never* happen. I think it's always an accident, you know. People just meet, and they fall in love, all by accident!" This really blows his mind. I'm trying to figure what this makes us – friends that fuck?

I'm relieved to know we've reached his great destination. Then he starts acting all romantic to contradict himself again.

"Can I come with you the next time you go to Laguna?" he asks. "I really like it down there, it would

Top: *An Elektra Records publicity shot of The Doors.*
Left to right: Jim Morrison, John Densmore, Robby Krieger, and
(lower right) Ray Manzarek. Bottom: *An informal early*
shot (c. 1967). Densmore sports a mustache,
Krieger a mustache and short beard.

At The Scene, New York City, 1967.

An Elektra Records pose of Morrison.

BETH KOCH

Judy Huddleston: teenager and model (1968-74).

APPLETON

Morrison, c. 1968 or 1969, at the
Griffith Park Observatory, Los Angeles.

Morrison with guitarist Krieger.

Elektra Records captures Morrison in a pensive mood.

A bearded and overweight Morrison, c. 1970.

be like a weekend vacation. I could meet your mother, too."

"Yeah, sure, there's plenty of room" I say, totally confused.

"Have a good weekend," he smiles mistily, getting out of the car.

As I'm pulling away from the curb, Jim lopes over to my open window and plants a deep kiss on my lips.

I drive away, convinced that he's incomprehensible, promising myself I'll never again attempt to understand anything he says or does. When I turn on the radio, his new single is playing.

CHAPTER 12

ALL ALONG THE WATCHTOWER

I'M GLAD TO RETURN TO HOLLYWOOD early Sunday night. The weekend has been a series of quick, anxious glances accompanied by philosophical statements of sorrow. Loss is temporary: Have a hotdog, a beer, look at the lovely, gleaming sea. Now, alone, I can wash and set my hair, good solid chores; the routine serves as its own eraser.

When Kathy returns, we talk about her weekend, try to make sense of it, then attempt to dissect Jim's behavior into a pattern. We finally abandon both pursuits and go to bed.

Five-thirty in the morning brings shuffling, laughter, indiscreet door slamming and generally raucous noises to the front door. Then there is a knock – more the sound of a falling body than a falling hand, but nevertheless, a knock. I open the door to find Jim collapsed against the wall. When he hears me, he snaps his head to attention and attempts to stand without using the wall. He is unmistakably drunk.

"We just got back from Mexico," he explains disjointedly, waving at the limousine sloppily parked in the street.

I'm frantically pulling the curlers out of my hair and throwing them behind me. After I've finished and my appearance is saved, I relax. Jim says he wouldn't have made it back without his great new friend, and insists this savior-chauffeur must come in, too.

"But my roommate's here." I object.

Snorting impatiently, Jim bolts from his postion on the porch and staggers across the small front lawn, twirling his Mexican straw hat on one finger. Throwing the hat in the air and catching it with whoops of pleasure, Jim dances in a lopsided circle. Aiming for the limo, he yelps, loses balance, and wildly tosses the hat. It lands forlornly on the sidewalk. His performance ended, Jim turns back to me.

"My friend doesn't have anyone! I can't just leave him! Don't you love me?" Jim asks, holding it over me like a weapon.

"Okay. Let me ask Kathy."

As Jim walks in, Kathy wakes up, saying "I just had a dream someone was trying to murder me." She sees Jim mid-sentence, and her face fills with embarrassed disbelief.

"That just about cuts the mustard!" Jim retorts, turning dramatically to leave, offended and unwanted again.

"Oh, come on, Jim," I say, catching his arm. "This is my friend, Kathy."

"Hi," she says, sitting up to rub her eyes in mild shock.

"Kathy," Jim says, seizing her hand. "I have this problem. See, Judy here doesn't want my friend, who drove me all the way home from Mexico, to come inside with me. Do you think that's fair?" he asks, glancing reproachfully at me.

"What time is it?" she asks.

"Nearly six A.M., time for America to rise and shine!"

"We might as well get up, we're already awake. 'Captain Kangaroo's' on pretty soon," she says.

"Oh good, let's all have a party!" Jim beams, beckoning his friend from the doorway. Temporarily elated, Jim jumps off the porch, calling to his friend.

"Judy, he's really drunk!" Kathy says.

"Oh, God," I sigh, leaning against the door. "I'm sorry. I've never seen him this bad. Really." My voice drops as Jim comes stumbling back up the steps, a tall, thin man trailing reluctantly behind him.

"No lights! No lights!" Jim cries, shielding his ward from the imaginary glare of cameras. "This, ladies," he bows, gesturing with his elbow to the young man beside him, "is the Mayor Sam Yorty's only son, traveling incognito. This is a government secret, of course, so he's impersonating that Latin ladies' man, Don Juan."

Don Juan is barely able to muster a wary smile before collapsing wearily in a corner chair. A long self-consious silence follows. Jim begins to weave back and forth across the room, apparently balancing on an invisible tightrope. Pausing deliberately, he makes a graceful spin, snakes up and down the hall, nearly trips and retrieves his balance in mid-air. I'm amazed and infuriated by this state of grace he maintains, turning stumbles into seemingly intentional dance steps, even when barely conscious.

"This isn't much of a *party*," he mumbles, glaring pointedly at me.

Kathy and I exchange glances, hardly the charming early-morning hostesses he's expected.

Singing sullenly to himself, Jim veers off into the kitchen, the cabinets and refrigerator slam open and shut and he shouts, "Nothing to drink!"

Then the radio turns on, a few notes come out full blast, he acknowledges it's a good station, and immediately shuts it off. Rushing out of the kitchen, he yells, "Where's my hat?"

Don Juan, who is having trouble keeping his eyes open, starts to attention.

"Where is it?" Jim wails.

"I don't know, man." Don Juan shrugs apologetically.

"Jesus. If there was a woman here, she'd take care of me!" Jim laments. "She'd give me a bath!"

"Your hat's on the sidewalk," I mutter.

Leaving the door open, Jim runs outside, then, flourishing his hat, slams back inside, and starts arranging the hat on Don Juan's head.

"A pirate, a cowboy . . . a desperado!" he exclaims, adjusting the brim to fit different characters. "A conquistador," he cries, pleased.

Don Juan coughs, and begins a wheezing laughter spree before becoming silent again.

Jim starts telling jokes that lack punch lines, sense, and delivery, though he responds to one about a blind man before a window with chillingly hollow laughter.

"Do either of you have any silk dresses?" he asks. "You know, the kind that drape and cling?"

"Not here," Kathy says, and I look mutely at the floor.

Dismissing us, Jim goes off into a rambling, semipoetic dissertation about the eternal mystery of a woman's body veiled in clinging, sheer silk. Kathy starts shooting him distasteful looks, and I've assumed the blank face of a model. Ignoring this nonreceptive audience, Jim keeps going until Kathy switches on the TV, angrily changing channels until she settles down engrossed before some cartoons.

"Hey – you can't do that! This is Saint Patrick's Day," Jim yells, turning off the television. "We're supposed to be celebrating for the wee people of Ireland! Doesn't anyone *care*?"

"You're a descendant of the Leprechauns?" Kathy snickers.

"It's not funny – it's the truth! I know," Jim declares, insulted. "In any case, we're celebrating for them." This is more a command than a whim. He defiantly takes out his Mexican reds and whites, splitting them up in meticulous halves.

Under the cloak of polite ceremony, we're supposed to swallow these for his ancestry. His harshly insistent mood leaves no room for argument. The pills are readily consumed, though this brings no alleviation to his bitter sarcasm and obnoxious remarks. Feeling cold and analytical, I stare at him.

"What are *you* looking at?" Jim asks.

"Nothing," I say, but seeing the glittering contempt in his eyes, change my mind. "Does it have to be so bad?"

"We *all* have our run-over dogs," he mutters, regarding me with scorn.

My love annihilated in one cruel swoop, I cut him off, refusing to react. He turns quickly to Kathy.

"We're all lost, aren't we?" he demands, reaching for her wrist. Not wanting to be pulled under, she shrugs him away.

"I don't know what you mean," she says.

"You know what I mean – *lost*!" he digs in persistently.

"No, I don't." Kathy glares at him and walks into the kitchen.

"Cunt," Jim comments, presumably to Don Juan. "I want some of that holy wine with the nun in the field." Laughing caustically, he glances at me in bewilderment, his eyes holding an appeal for mercy.

I'M UNABLE TO SUBJECT MYSELF TO HIS demanding, inarticulate need anymore. Speechless, I get up and leave the room. In the back room, I climb into the walk-in closet, close the door behind me, and curl into a fetal position. I will stay there forever, or until Jim leaves, whichever comes first.

Kathy finds me crying over a circular leather emblem I once made and beaded with a serpent spitting fire. I'd done it in some romantically absurd revery over Jim.

"Judy, what are you doing here?" she asks incredulously.

"Sleeping," I sulk.

"We thought you had just disappeared!" Kathy's brown eyes are warm with concern.

"Is he gone yet?" I ask, shifting positions on the floor.

"No. He's just given up. We went to the Hollywood Ranch Market. It was the only place open with the right wine, J&B, cheese and vodka." Kathy sounds suspiciously high.

"Who went?"

"Me and John, that's Don Juan's name. He told me all about how Jim doesn't think anyone loves him for his true self. Everyone just uses him. He can't trust anyone anymore. He doesn't even think he has any friends!"

"I wonder why," I snort cynically.

Kathy looks at me reprovingly. "I don't think you're being very fair," she says in measured, liberal tones. She's feeling very touched and sorry for Poor Jim.

"You could at least be civil and come out of the closet!"

"Is he still drunk and obnoxious?" I ask.

"No, he's real quiet and sad. I *told* you, he gave up and thought you'd left! Now he's just sitting there, and I'm getting breakfast together. Besides, I think he likes you," she adds before bounding out of the room, leaving me no choice but to follow.

I creep cautiously down the hall, wanting to spare my wounded pride further damage. Kathy has put on "Captain Kangaroo," her favorite early-morning escape; it's successfully easing the previously unbearable tension. I welcome the meaningless televison drone; TV does have its merits.

Jim looks up at me as if I'm an hallucination and smiles. He's obviously forgotten his earlier behavior.

"Hi, honey, will you make me a cup of coffee?" Jim purrs as though we're an old-married, or a just married couple, or *some* couple.

Kathy has gone to the café across the street to buy him something good and expensive for breakfast. She wants to make sure he won't think any of us want him for his money or fame or whatever else he has. The coffee, hash browns, sausage, scrambled eggs and muffins make him amiable.

"You're a real champ," he congratulates Kathy.

"Yeah, that's what they called me in high school," she remarks.

She goes to put the fifth of scotch, fifth of vodka and the Blue Nun away, which will apparently remain unopened, even though it was the entire purpose of the trip to the market.

"I really appreciate what you're doing for me," Jim says, becoming more docile and sweet by the second. "Oh, I'm so comfortable now, I couldn't ask for more,"

Jim murmurs, contentedly forgetting his previous hostility in hell. He kisses me on the cheek, sprawls out indecorously across my bed, closes his eyes and falls asleep.

Emerging from the kitchen, where he's been attempting to seduce Kathy, Don Juan follows Jim's cue and konks out on Kathy's bed. This is all so exciting. Kathy and I look at each other, tiptoe around the apartment, and silently flee out the door.

AFTER MAKING THE MUTUAL DISCOVERY that reds aren't the thing to take before painting, Kathy and I leave Choinard early. My overly liberated hand has managed to ruin any internal logic once existing on my canvas. We conclude the only possible retreat is a Mexican café, where we can dawdle and slowly wake.

The hours pass. I'm the personification of guilty indecision. I feel heartless, I feel sorry, I feel angry, I want to help him, I want him to get lost. Coping with him threatens my sanity, but not coping with him threatens my existence. The difference is negligible. When we finally return home at five that afternoon, I hope Jim's there as much as I hope he's not.

CHAPTER 13

THE CIRCLE GAME

YOU MEAN YOU JUST LEFT US? JUST LEFT us here, all alone?" is Jim's reaction when Kathy and I finally return. They're both still sitting there, looking stoned.

"What were we supposed to do? Sit around and watch you sleep?" I say.

Unable to think of an adequate comeback, Jim contents himself by looking crucified. Beginning to feel like a deserting, careless bitch, I sit down beside him in the form of an apology. This trifling movement causes Don Juan to believe we're finally pairing off, and he follows Kathy everywhere, kissing her behind the ears, murmuring Latin lover lies. Becoming paranoid, she calls an old boyfriend for protection, and he invites her to Palm Springs. Don Juan pouts as she packs.

When Kathy calls her father and invents a witty, conversational story of what she's supposedly doing, Jim bolts up to attention.

"And I thought I wanted a daughter!" he says in disgust.

Kathy sends her most polished look of scorn. Poor Jim seems to be wearing thin on her. By the time she leaves, Jim has collapsed again, and her attempted introduction falls on deaf ears. Her boyfriend regards Jim as a scientific specimen, although his calm detachment is stripped when Jim, falling upside-down and backwards, merrily waves and loudly chortles, "Goodbye, goodbye!" The door closes to Kathy's stifled giggling.

All I want to do is wake Jim up, so I start kissing his face. Being infantile, he responds naturally with gurgling childlike noises. Alarmed, I stare in sacreligious revulsion, not liking the mole by his nose, or his ears. For a moment I wonder what I ever saw in this sniveling brat. With a mournful sigh, Don Juan lurches from the far corner, gives me one greedy look and nods goodbye, so as not to wake the baby, and leaves. Just as the engine turns over outside, Jim awakens, wildly transforming his energy from an inert rock to a lightning rod and bolts out the front door. Yelling, "Stop! Stop!" he runs down the street.

Compelled to watch, I walk out on the front steps. Jim is waving his arms insanely – as if to stop the world, not merely his departing friend, but it doesn't work in either case. Dropping his arms, he sinks to the curb with an air of complete dejection and futility. Under the flickering streetlamp, he's the archetypal lost soul, crying cold and defeated in the gutter. He looks so wretched, it's pathetic, and I walk out into the damp evening to sit beside him in silence. I don't know what to say, but I know he can't even *speak* as we stare at the thin, muddy water running down a storm drain.

"Jim, I really do like you," I finally manage.

"Good. I like you too! Let's go out to dinner," he suggests, cheerfully changing character. This Jim is not in the least morbid, he's smiling and slightly giddy, bounding up from the street. "I know where we can have good Italian food, you'll love it!" he says, humming as we walk across the lawn.

As we go inside he starts up a ludicrous, lighthearted jingle: "We're in the city now, we can't go barefoot now."

Laughing, I gather it's a new cowboy song or a subtle hint I'd better not look like I just stepped off the bus from Arkansas. As I put on my suede jacket and boots in the hallway, he pulls me over to the oval mirror, and surveys our appearance as a whole.

He smiles at it, then looking worried, asks, "Are you taller than me?"

I assure him I am not, for at least the fifth time, to date. His preoccupation with my height is boundless, you'd think I was an Amazon and he was a midget.

I DRIVE KATHY'S CAR, A LARGE CONVERTible that gives Jim lots of room to sprawl as he carries on a serious monologue about women. He's got some philosophy going that women are the noble creatures who carry on your name and family with dignity after you die.

"Women are like depths of compassion." Jim nearly swoons over this poetic delight, and I think it's pretty romantic, for an idea. I have never felt like a depth of compassion. But maybe I'm too young.

"Chicks," he tells me, "have a comic approach to life." He sounds puzzled and envious.

So am I. I could use a comic approach – now that I see I'm misplaced as a female entirely, neither a chick nor a woman. Ladies live in English castles, so that's out.

"You know," Jim continues, "what I need is a woman who would just laugh at me. One who wouldn't take me seriously, I mean the things I do, the stupid things, she would just *laugh*."

I can't see this expectation being filled, especially if you take into consideration the "stupid things" he does. I glance sideways to see if he's joking, but he's not; he has this yearning look that accompanies his deepest delusions. He must be crazy to imagine some earth-mother wonder would dare mess around with him, only morons would have that nerve. I'm now a disenchanted moron, listening to the gravel under the tires as we pull into the parking lot.

"You don't mind driving? No, you're a good driver. You know they say I'm dangerous driving." He sighs loudly at what a wreck he is. "I had to stop, I'm too irresponsible. It's just that I can't concentrate on anything in specific that long."

When we get out of the car, the air is fresh and clean, revitalizing. Everything has turned new and we're both smiling and excited, talking gibberish, feeling good for no reason. An old gay guy is walking down the narrow gravel alley in front of us, he's trying real hard to look young. "I wonder how it feels to be an aging homosexual," Jim says.

"Aging, I guess," I say. "I thought you were bi or something, anyway. Someone said so." I'm being quite friendly about it; I'm just curious, but he gets cold as hell.

"That guy must've been projecting," says Mr. Frosty Voice.

"What guy?" asks the aging dumb blonde.

Taking a path to the front of the restaurant, we emerge on a busy sidewalk, under bright lights, and stare at each other.

"The guy who told you!" Jim pauses dramatically, giving me a full-on shot of hopelessness. We even have to stop for it, to get the right angle before he says, "I'm *hopelessly heterosexual.*"

Judging from his facial expression, this must be a terrible predicament. I look appropriately sympathetic and let the subject drop. We're still standing in front of a restaurant called Don Taña's; a few doors down is The Troubadour.

Gaining his composure, Jim leads me inside to a corner booth. Having avoided calamity, he soars into his gracious, man of the world role, handling the waiters and wine with wit and style. We drink and get romantic and dramatic. This lasts until he finds out all I want to eat is soup.

"I bet you're not really hungry! If you hadn't *deserted* us and left me alone like that, this wouldn't be happening. I bet all you did was eat all day. And you're not hungry! It's true isn't it?"

"No. I'm just not that hungry," I lie. He's right. I've never been into eating like a sparrow. I'm stuffed.

"Well, I'll bet it wasn't as good as what you could have had here!" He's pleased with this as just punishment.

Recuperating with a few sips of wine, he gets soft and sweet, thinking maybe he's falling in love with me. "Could you be faithful to me?"

"If I wanted to."

"No. I'm serious. You know sometimes I might leave you a few months at a time. And I want to meet all women. Even her!" He points to an almost fat, loudly dressed, basically ugly woman across the room. I wrinkle my nose, unimpressed. "That's it! I want to see what she's like. Not *her*, really. But I can't help it. And I'll bet you could never wait. You could never wait that long."

"I could too!" I blunder into vanity's trap. Now my pride has made me a confessed fool, he's won the game.

"Your roommate is really cute. Maybe all three of us should get together sometime." He leers sadistically, waiting for my next dumb comment.

"No," I say carefully, "Kathy wouldn't want to do that. She tried it before once, and she didn't like it. At all."

"She must have liked it." Jim uses his remarkable logic. "Otherwise, she wouldn't remember it."

"Why don't you just get someone for *me*?" I ask defiantly. "I think I'd like that better."

"That wouldn't be quite the same," he mumbles lamely.

"Why not?" I'm becoming belligerent.

"It just wouldn't be." He shrugs it away, uncomfortable with my attitude.

"What I want to do is start a new religion. That's what I really want to do." I had suspected something of the kind, but am afraid to ask what the *basis* of the religion would be. "But first" he adds, "I want to be a movie star." He makes it all sound misty and dreamlike.

"Won't it look sort of stupid? I mean, people will laugh – a movie star starting a new religion. You know?" I ask. It's already embarrassing enough the way he's always getting arrested for obscenity or something.

"Yeah, I know." Jim sounds semi-resigned to those who do not appreciate chameleons. "Do you know that Frank Sinatra song? The one about getting older and wiser but having done it the way he wanted? Have you listened to the lyrics, I mean, really?" I nod. "That's all I want."

If only he weren't so damn sincere, if only he didn't care so much. Feeling tormented by the depth of his relentless dreams, I nervously burst out my LSD arrest story, emphasizing how I'd felt the blue veins on my wrist were him and life itself.

"I think you must have gotten that from Pam," he interrupts before I'm finished. "She has this thing about her hands; she thinks they're going to be cut off or something. A fear of damaged fingers."

"But I don't even *know* Pam!"

"It would come from me, really – but through her. That's all." He makes it sound so simple and obvious, I must be really slow not to get it. "I'm sure you got it from her." He diagnoses this like some psychic venereal disease.

"What's she like?" I don't want to know, but I have to ask, especially now that we've got this great bond.

"She's always giving me trouble." Jim launches into instant complaints. "She's always disturbing me – on purpose. To make me react; she's always trying to make me *react*."

"Well, that's . . . "

"So I don't." He's proud of this reaction, then his irritation retreats and the guilt comes up. "I mean she's been everything to me. She's been my mother, my sister, my daughter, my friend and lover."

I'm beginning to feel nauseated; I hadn't asked for all the gory details.

"Every time we start to live together, I'm optimistic. Maybe I'm too idealistic, but it just never works out." He sighs. "I love her. I'm just not in love with her."

I'm torn between jealousy and sympathy towards Pam, unable to find a solid stance. Confused, I retreat into a shell of alienation. I don't know if I'd really care to be in her place, it sounds pretty unrewarding for all the time it must take.

"I don't feel I've ever seen the real you," I hear Jim saying, bringing me back, up, and out of myself. His voice has a note of challenge.

"That's probably true." I'm relieved. I want so much for him to see the real me, whatever that is. "I'm really shy," I say, thinking this is the clue to my personality.

"You — shy?" He snorts at this pure impossiblitiy, tracing my breast lightly, as if it's proof of my daring.

"Yes! I really am," I insist, drawing back, offended. "I ran away with my first real boyfriend. My father hated him because I loved him."

But Jim thinks my father was behaving logically (I did lose my virginity, didn't I?). Then he crosses over the invisible sex line, telling me what great sex we are going to have from now on. He's getting enchanted with his revelations.

"What you should do — is just be really luxurious."

"Luxurious?"

"Like a little girl, crawling around with that unselfconscious sexuality." After hearing this new definition of luxury, I'm given time to digest it before he continues. "Also, I think it would really help you to just lay around and suck my cock, for hours."

"Yeah, if I can ever come too."

"Well, it's hardly like a guy ejaculating!" he says, scornfully.

I glare back in equal contempt, wondering if he knows I've passed my thirteenth birthday. Evidently not. He must feel it's his duty to tell women how they do or don't come.

"Why did you have to do that 'I Have a Cock' performance in Miami?" I spit out.

"That isn't important. I'm tired of it." Looking defensive, he waves it away, trying to appear bored.

I keep staring at him, expecting an answer, and he fidgets under my gaze.

The war of the sexes is getting stronger than Jim cares

for, he reaches for my hand under the table. Lowering his voice, he says, "I don't know, I can't help it." He searches my eyes, making them soften, hunting for the romance again, and I am, too.

I'm supposed to be the understanding, forgiving one, to the point of jumping out of my identity into his. And I do. The feeling is recaptured as the waiters begin casting us It's-closing-time looks. Jim is irritated by this.

"They're too blatant. I like to be the last to leave." Nevertheless, he gets up, looking snotty, and says, "Let's leave!"

WE GO TO THE TROUBADOUR, WHERE I feel attacked by eyes. I hope I don't look like another one of those naïve girls who don't know about him. I want to scream, "I know, I know, I know!" However, I will treat this as another hallucination instead.

An utterly frenzied, hostile cocktail waitress has come yelling to Jim. "Don't start *that* shit again!"

He's just peeked around the corner to see what is on stage. They are obviously old, intimate enemies. I'm scared of her, glad to escape to the bar, where Jim orders a margarita for himself and tells me I'm too drunk to drink any more. Infuriated, I flirt with some friend of his who's giving me a "Is he giving you a hard time?" line. Catching this, Jim icily tells the guy to cool it and, thus reducing me to property, possessively steers me away to a group of overly hip-looking men. They are, I soon surmise, old drinking partners.

Blanking out by progressive degrees, I'm merely aware of being a female in a totally male atmosphere. Jim's Miami bust has turned into "a humorous bit of politics that got out of hand," which he seems to find entertaining as hell.

Looking around the room reflectively, the grey strands in his beard standing out, Jim asks, "I wonder what it will be like when we're in our thirties and people respect us?"

Another question no one can answer. Then he's ordering another drink, starting the cycle up, beginning to laugh at nothing.

He takes me aside and says, "I'm going to be here for a while, and this will just bore you. So you might as well go home now, and I'll come back later." He pauses uncertainly, then says, "I still love you and everything." This declaration is said straight out loud.

I am definitely shocked. He has never even said he loved me, and now he loves me *still*?

I smile weakly, too tired to keep up with him. I know he's been caught up on a new wheel, of faces and places, and what happens with them. He needs an extra dose – an extra dose of everything. I just want to go home and sleep. And hope he shows up when the circle's through – this one, or the next.

CHAPTER 14

FOR WHAT IT'S WORTH

IT'S NOT SURPRISING TO WAKE UP ALONE the next morning. I get up, dress, drive to school. Unfortunately, I've read that artists are sad characters, and have taken it to heart. The teachers praise my "personal and dedicated" art and give me A's, but all I'm really dedicated to is the upkeep and maintenance of my fantasy world (in case the other goes bad). It is sanity insurance.

Today, I would do better in a padded room than a painting studio. Every time I time I attempt to speak, I lapse into giggling fits.

Soon enough, I'm at my front door. The telephone is ringing, causing me a near nervous breakdown while I jam the key into the locked door. Once inside, I bolt across the room, breathlessly picking up the receiver. I am expecting God. At the moment, God is available in the form of a hesitant girl's voice, "Hello? Is this Judy?"

"Yes." I'm terribly disappointed.

"This is the secretary for The Doors. Jim said he may have left his notebook at your house." She sounds apologetic, embarrassed and shy. Also, there is a strange questioning feeling coming off her words. "Do you know if it's there?"

"Yeah, it's on the floor."

I remember skimming through it last night and finding it incomprehensible, full of a lot of ha-ha-ha's. There was one big scrawl, "Therefore, time does not exist," and something resembling a screenplay about billboards and bathrooms on Sunset Boulevard. I was too sleepy to really get interested. His Mexican hat is sitting next to it, too.

"They're having a session now. He needs it; there are some new songs in it. Could you possibly drop it off?"

"Sure," I say. I would drop myself off parcel-post if asked. "I'm only a few minutes away."

"Oh, thank you. I really appreciate it." Maybe I just spared her some horrendous task, like doing it herself. She sounds relieved when we hang up.

I have no intelligence to speak of, I don't stop to sit down, breathe slowly, recollect who I am, where I am, or what I'm doing. I simply plunge ahead, not thinking, the habit of impulsiveness driving me. I check out my appearance, find it satisfactory, and emerge into the world a blithering idiot. A few minutes later, I arrive as promised, and hand over the notebook. Bill sees me and asks if I'll come into his office.

After a brief preface assuring me I look good, he announces, "You know, Jim just *disappeared* for three days."

"I know. He was with me." I answer this accusation of Jim's unreliability too quickly, too defensively. Bill shakes his head at me.

"Well, when he *left*, he was with another girl. I saw her. She was just as good looking as you, and smart." He gives me an awful piercing look, his point made.

I stare at him, thinking: But I'm different. I don't want to know anything that ruins this persistent idea. Bill opens the door and points to the secretary sitting in front.

"*She* loves him, too. She came all the way from the East Coast."

I inspect her defiantly, then stick out my tongue to prove my maturity.

"But he's never given her a reason to believe," Bill adds. At least he knows I've been handed a few measly reasons.

Bill closes the door, sits down, and shakes his head again.

"You don't know how many secretaries have had to leave because of him. At first, they think they can save him, then they see him coming in, raking himself over the coals. Day after day. No one can really help him. I don't know, either he'll end up a refined, mellow guy – or in the gutter. Don't think I don't love him, I've just seen a lot of it," he says.

"But I *love* him!" My statement sounds meaningless. I'm beginning to shake, the tears are about to brim over, ruining my composure.

"I know." Bill's voice is hollow. "But I just don't think Jim can really relate to women. Except Pam, I guess. I don't really know what their gig is." He shrugs in distaste, probably for my benefit. "I don't know what he sees in her. She's always crying. But she helped him a lot in the old days, you know, when he was first getting started. It's too bad you didn't meet him then."

My pride is slowly slipping off in liquid layers, soon it'll be a puddle on the floor. My shaking increases perceptibly. Bill gets up and puts his arms around me.

"I just can't give up."

Bill doesn't answer. I know that my refusal to let go

of a dream until it's smashed to pieces is unanswerable. I wipe at my face and back off, trying to smile.

"I better leave now." I'm getting nervous. I don't want Jim to see me in this state.

"Take care of yourself." Bill hugs me goodbye. He did his best.

I walk through the room and down the staircase like a model down a runway. I may be petrified sick, held together by loose pins, but no one would ever guess. Unless they happened to meet me halfway through the show, on the middle landing by the geraniums, like Jim.

"Hello," he says, waiting for a reply.

A reply? My lungs are bursting for air, just standing is a feat in itself. His pleased-to-see-me look has turned to confusion. As my silence mounts, he grows more puzzled and expectant.

"Thanks for bringing my book," he says, finally. "I would have called or come over, but we were really busy."

"You didn't come back," I hear myself saying. Only I have rocky frog's croak that breaks at a high, static pitch. It's almost as remarkable as the sentence I've just stuttered out.

"I stayed with some friends," he says.

"Oh . . . I hope you had a nice time!"

This is supposed to be sincere, to negate my opening croak, and imply I have no intentions of hampering his freedom. It comes off phony. I should run away before I utter another syllable.

His body is in the way, cornering me. Any semblance of poise has left. Jim never knew I was an absolute moron. This excuse for a conversation turns into off-key vibrations; flying arrows missing the target.

I feel like a scroungy dog caught off-guard with a

secret and no bone. And the secret is terrifying. I have put everything crucial, ideal, beautiful – into one image. The image is Him. I am in a state of solid worship.

He doesn't know that, mere human that he is. He just keeps staring at me. I stutter out something to the effect that I am going. He moves aside, an unsettled note permeating the air, though we pretend everything is fine, maybe just a little odd. Some goodbye is uttered and I make it to the car. I get in and see him turn to walk back inside.

Not satisfied with making a fool of myself, I now make a total ass of myself. I walk after him, preparing to correct the mess, and enter a room full of smoky faces and blaring music.

Reverting to my mannequin routine, I softly say, "Kathy's still in Palm Springs, come by whenever you're free."

He nods his head, looking down at a page of words and keeping time to the music. I exit.

I drive home, walk straight into the bathroom, and lock the door behind me. Falling down and across the smooth, cool tiles, I throw my arms around the hanging towel. It is soft. I grasp onto it as though it were all the strength in the world, I need it transfused through my blood. It's a ghost Madonna, my father's chest, my mother's skirt, God's understanding – a towel. I can't let go of it, as my body fills with bitter, wracking pain. It is deep, pouring in continuously, pouring out continuously: it has no end. I can't tell if it began from within or without me. I *am* it.

There's a sudden, rope-burning twist inside me that's totally physical; my heart is being ripped apart, the edges red and seared, raw, wrenched open in convulsive waves. I am making the most, unearthly sobbing noises I have ever heard. It's all so involuntary, I feel I am going to die. After a final climax, the pain ripples out and leaves.

I am exhausted from fighting, or giving in. I curl into a ball on the floor, wondering why I was never told broken hearts are not a poetic metaphor, but a literal activity. I pull the towel down next to me for a pillow. I fall asleep, knowing I won't see Jim for weeks . . . months . . .

SUMMER THEREFORE COINCIDES WITH MY heart breaking. Kathy and I pay up our summer rent, to avoid the fall rush of house hunting. She leaves for New Mexico, I leave for Laguna Beach. In 1969 Laguna is a veritable mecca for hippies. The place is teeming over with brown rice, pregnant earth mothers and their old men who buy and sell miscellaneous psychedelics, embroidered clothes, incense and organic vegetables.

I suffer mild culture shock (I am not a hippie, I am too screwed up). I feel combined guilt, hostility, and rebellion towards the enlightened ones. They've set up a new norm, and I don't fit it, either.

My girlfriend, Linda, has become full-fledged hippie of pure intent. She introduces me to the people of the village, hoping I will come out of my catatonic coma. It just makes me worse. I can't believe that the city gave birth to smog, jealousy, politics, meat-eating and other bad things. I can't passively accept each new day as glorious. In the middle of the gentle flow around me, I want to scream, "You're hypocrites!"

In homespun, embroidered clothes, with no make-up and my hair hanging loose and moppy, I'm viewed as a sister; but if I wear make-up, curl my hair, and eat at Taco Bell, I'm a spiritual reject. I do both on purpose, and, I am amazed at the reactions my surface image causes. People actually believe you are what you look like. This seems dumb, since it's easy to change that twenty times a day.

The summer passes slowly, a hot cocoon to bear out until the shedding and release of fall. I'm confronted with a few more psyche doctors jabbing needles of "You'd be better if only . . . " but summer ends, and I gleefully take off for the corrupt city where I can be miserable in peace.

CHAPTER 15

BLUE BOY

I AM BACK IN LOS ANGELES FOR A FEW weeks before receiving Jim's first three-in-the-morning call. He doesn't bother to announce himself, just says, "Judy?" and this affirmed, cries out, "I'm lonely!" There is a pause to enable his despair to sink effectively into my already damaged brain cells. Getting more hopeful, and to the point he asks, "Will you come and make love with me? Please?"

I don't answer; I stare into the dark, wondering why my heart is beating too fast.

"I've come by your place, and you're never there! I thought you'd almost moved or something." This avowal tips the scales; willpower seems absurd.

"Okay, I'll come over. Where are you, anyway?"

"At the office. And I'm cold! Will you bring a blanket?"

"Uh huh."

"Really? You'll even bring a blanket?" I guess this is all beyond his wildest dreams.

"Yeah. It's red with a black stripe, and it's not even itchy!"

"Are you making fun of me? Are you really going to come?"

"I said I was. I just have to get dressed and stuff."

"Good. Remember the blanket. I'm not even drunk!" With this great declaration, he hangs up.

I dress recklessly as Kathy sighs loudly, gives me a nauseated look, and flops over on her stomach in disgust. This, apparently, is not a relationship to be encouraged.

Soon, I'm in my car, complete with the blanket, driving up the deserted streets. My heart pounds madly through the echoing silence, waiting for dawn, going to the man on the other side; my child, lover, furnisher of take-me-to-the-Nile dreams. And I think hippies are weird. Put me on a plate, probe me with a needle, and my one word will be "Jim."

He is exuberant at my arrival. He must've been looking out the window or listening, because the second I pull up, he runs outside naked, hangs his body over the railing and waves wildly. I get out, vaguely surprised and wonder if he'll fall off.

"You're beautiful!" he shouts, "beautiful!" He seems a bit delirious. "Take off your clothes!" Jim continues his mad rhapsody. "I want to see all of you!"

This seems an excellent idea – I'm an exhibitionist at heart, and my long flowing, Greek goddess stuck-in-the-wrong-time-zone clothes are perfect for elegant disrobing in a parking lot.

"Oh, you're really beautiful!" Jim is having a great time endangering his life and applauding me.

I do my nude-ascending-the-staircase wonderfully. It's just too bad it isn't midday so we could bring entertainment back to those caught on boring lunch breaks.

Once inside, I see Jim is in one of his full-blown, romantic X-rated soap opera moods. Standing on the opposite side of the room, he issues questions.

"Haven't you missed me? Hasn't it been a long time?"

His eyes bore into mine, his magnetism hypnotizes me, causing me to walk trance-like and speechless across the space separating us. He puts his arms around me, enfolding, molding me to him. My head is tilted back, his fingers play over the contours of my face until he pulls my body stronger against his, suddenly passionate without role-playing. He has lost himself, surrendered to the moment, without trying. His sincerity almost blows me away, turns me to wind, to silver-blue. This must be the kiss all perfumes are aiming for, the incredible, irrepeatable, unforgettable.

But it breaks, and he comes back. He remembers he is a director-performer, and I'm his spectator-actress. We fall down on the red, itchless blanket spread across the floor – as if for a picnic, and get down to the first theatre piece of the morning. This is a short melodrama in which we are both cast as mad, wildly lustful animals. I can only see myself as a lion or a horse, which makes it hard to relate. My imagination isn't currently sufficient to get that I'm just an animal-person. So I watch him. He's really trying hard to convince himself he is an animal. Period, that's all.

"I'm an animal. I'm an animal – an animal!" he screams at me. "Do you understand?"

"Yes!"

"I'm an animal!" He gets over the novelty of this, and changes scenes. It's an old one, the dialogue is slightly updated.

"Whose girl are you?"

"Yours."

"Are you only my girl?"

"Yes."

"I own you! You're mine!" he elaborates. I think this is pushing it, but he's getting demonic, stressing it. "I own you, I own you – don't I?"

"Yes." I sound bored, although I'm actually feeling a combination of fear and resentment.

Instead of making him mad, my lack of enthusiasm unnerves him. Jim forgets about his stage in an attempt to regain my interest. First he tries some meaningless romantic murmur, "You and me, Judy."

I guess this is supposed to be suggestive, but it's just an incomplete sentence. He gets physical and goes down on me, another approach.

"I love your pussy," he says. I figure they're all the same, and remain unmoved.

"You're so beautiful!" I am really tired of that one.

"Just wait!" I spit out ferociously.

"Wait for what?" he asks, taken aback, totally confused, staring at me like I've lost my senses.

"Wait until you see what I'm really going to be like!"

"But there's nothing to wait for! You're already beautiful." He's insistent. "I can't see what there is to wait for!"

He must think this is my goal in life! All I am now is a young girl; I mean, wait 'til I'm grown up, you'll be shocked, you moron. But the whole thing escapes him, he just looks hurt as if I'm practicing evasion tactics on him. I decide I might as well be nice, I just can't relate to being an owned animal.

He goes off into his "Now, now, now" land instead. Then he starts to cry. They are real tears. He's so upset I can't believe it.

He gasps, "I never want this to end, I never want it to end!"

He works himself into a frenzy of more crying, more despair, because it is going to end, and he is going to die. Again.

After dying, Jim assumes his usual dignified air of sanity and walks over to the telephone to call some airline.

He hangs up, laughing, "Well, I just missed that flight to New York."

I'm too stunned from the movie to get the punchline. He's in a real uproar. I can't see what's so tremendously funny about the fact that he's not in New York, although he's supposed to be at a film festival there and everyone is probably sitting around waiting for him, thinking, Jim's disappeared again.

HE CONTINUES WALKING AROUND AIM-lessly, chortling to himself, as I attempt to stand. After finding my balance I walk to the window, and look out, feeling crushed by something. It's a dreary, uninspiring view.

Jim comes over to my side, looking serious and overcome with another nameless emotion. He takes my hand and sweetly says, "Isn't love nice?"

I can't imagine how these ridiculous words have come out of his mouth. I think love is horrid. It can kill you, and he thinks it's nice? I feel like a soft bird caught in his hands, one he could unconsciously mutilate with the slightest, most gentle pressure. My vibes aren't particularly uplifting, and he begins to look absolutely mournful.

Turning from the window, he looks into my eyes and says, "Would you marry me?"

This is a loaded question, but I haven't the wits for guile, and say yes.

This cheers him up considerably, I have to affirm it a few times. I guess he feels real, now that he knows he's a person someone would marry. He happily suggests we should go sit on the couch in the other room, where we can be more comfortable and talk.

I trail after him, wondering what's going on now. He has taken the blanket and spread it across the couch, where he's sitting, when I walk across the room.

"I can't believe how much you've changed! I mean you just used to be this funky little girl. Now, you're a movie star!"

I guess this is supposed to be a true progression, but I can't see myself as either of those characters.

My face must be doing strange things, for now he says, "I really mean it!"

That's just terrific, but what I really feel like is a nice, faithful dog, who pants along after her master, not exactly knowing why. Whether I'm an Afghan or a Shepherd is incidental. I go over to the couch, sit on the far end, and hide my body under the blanket.

He watches this little routine, then says, "I love you."

"Oh, I know. Just like a person loves their dog."

"No!" He's actually angry, maybe I should have explained I feel I'm quite an admirable, worth-loving dog. "I love you like a human being! I do," he says.

I don't see how he can love me as a human being, since he doesn't even know me, but I'm afraid to insult his integrity any further and shut up.

Pacified, he becomes childlike, asking, "Do you love me?"

"Yes."

"How come you never tell me then? If you really love

me, you'll have to prove it, by repeating it – one thousand times!" This, he finds a particularly brilliant invention.

"I love you, I love you, I love you, I love you, I," I am beginning to hope he isn't serious, "love you, I love . . . "

"How many men have you gone to bed with" Jim's fixation on my countless jealous lovers is about to go down the drain. My ruthless bad-girl image is in jeopardy.

"Four, counting you." I don't know if it sounds like a lot or a little.

"Four?"

"Yeah." I probaby should have said seventy-five or two hundred and eleven, or something.

"You're practically a virgin!" he bursts out, flushed. "I mean, I feel really privileged." He looks embarrassed and thrilled, like he's just made it with the Virgin Mary.

"Do you think maybe I'm too old for you?" His sin is reduced to child molestation.

"No. I think it's about right. You're only seven years older than me, I can't see what difference it makes. My dad is seven years older than my mom."

"I guess." Perplexed and doubtful, Jim asks, "What is Huddleston, anyway?"

"My last name."

"No, I mean what ancestry?"

"It's English. But my mother is French, and there's a feud over which part is Scottish or Irish." I might as well say Mongrel.

"I didn't think you were Jewish." He sounds relieved. I think that's sort of nasty and give him a dirty look.

"It's just that Jewish girls are on this weird trip, sometimes. I don't get along with them very well."

"Oh."

"I think we should go to the woods together. For a weekend. I know these woods where we could go. Do you want to?"

"Yeah, I love the woods. My first backyard was a lot of woods. I feel good there."

I'm going off into fantasies about the freedom of those days, while Jim curls himself up next to me, pulling the blanket up over us. He mumbles something about us needing sleep, and is soon gone, leaving me awake and staring at a calendar. I drowsily compute performance dates, while my mind runs a "this will never last" tape, over and over. It switches off to a knock-your-head-against-the-wall emotion. I know I can never really reach him, he'll never really believe that I do honestly love him. I could go down on my knees, cry testimony to God, beg him to believe, but somehow it feels he never will.

I have drifted off for a few hours when Jim noisily awakes, good humored, and ready for the day. After I've dressed and am brushing my hair, he comes up with another awe-struck "You have such good taste" remark. I don't know why he finds this so damn remarkable, it seems slightly offensive.

"Oh, don't start that ritual up again!" I say.

"Don't get all huffy about it!" he protests. "You know, pretty soon people will be arriving here. And you don't want them to come in and see us all naked and crazy, do you?"

"No. Not really."

At this, he happily pulls my top down to my waist, beginning a wild attempt to put me in a frenzy. I come up for a gasp of air and give him an evil glance. He laughs, he has made a mess of me on purpose. I glare as I again straighten my appearance. He tells me tales of all the great movies he's going to take me to see. My mind goes blank when he comes up with promises I never ask for. I cynically wonder if this will all take place before or after we go to the woods. Still, half of me believes him, maybe more; this is infuriating. It makes me think what we have is more than a good time.

It's time for me to go off to school again, which also impresses him for some unknown reason. We walk downstairs. He's infatuated with whoever he thinks I am at the moment. We get to my car and I turn into a statue.

"You have green eyes!" he exclaims.

"I always have," I reply cooly.

"And you even look beautiful, in the morning like this!" Jim continues, undaunted. Then he hugs me, a big teddy-bear type hug, and says, "You're going to be my new girlfriend from now on, huh?"

"Uhm hmn," I agree, taken over by the sweet, tender feeling coming out of him. It seems especially intimate with the noisy traffic surrounding us, we seem more alone in that poignant, lovesick sense.

"You know," he says, holding me back to survey for a second, then pulling me close again, "it's not just the sex! I could just go on, holding you like this – forever. I never want to let you go!"

I smile and squirm away into my car. He is saying very dangerous things. I don't want to hear them run through my head at night when I'm trying to fall asleep. I remain calm, watching him lean over to look at me, a portrait of loving sincerity, as he says, "Have a good day," and kisses me goodbye, his star pupil.

CHAPTER 16

SUNSHINE OF MY LOVE

DURING THE NEXT MONTH, I BEGIN TO suffer from an unprecedented affliction. This malady, which comes visiting, madly producing colors and changing tones of the most mundane phenomena, I readily term "Reality Attacks." They occur with no rhyme or reason, finding their victim unprepared to combat them. I can be sitting, walking, talking, eating, drawing, anything, when a sudden siege of pure surreal symbolism will assail me; first hitting me in the stomach, then traveling in a frenzied adrenalin rush to my brain. I reel under this assault, becoming a faint, stricken Camille, staring in terrible amazement at whatever stark, simple thing is at my current eye-level. Talking is virtually impossible when having a Reality Attack, it is far beyond words.

Two of these seizures are particularly noteworthy, the second causes me to seek out a doctor, hoping for a cure. One takes place when I'm sitting alone in a car, waiting for Kathy and looking at the dark, stained Choinard parking lot pavement. My vision shifts upward to an object known as a car. Its massive thingness is astounding in itself, however, the large black patch spread across the ground in an upside-down, but perfect replica of the car's upright image is truly amazing. Hard-to-breathe symptoms set in. The car moves, causing an awkward, distorted distinction to take over the shadow.

My attention shifts to the Sun, the culprit. It is causing all this! A glowing red-orange ball of pure fire, suspended in the air. We're all traveling around these mad flames – just stuck up there, burning, causing the shadow under the car to move. I am, struck speechless, the essence of nature is hard to absorb without keeling over. How people go on functioning with these miracles constantly going on is beyond me.

I know I'm probably suffering from chemical recurrences, that I don't want to have a nervous breakdown and heart attack at twenty. I go to my cardiologist in Newport. He's not too thrilled with my wild haired, braless, red-shawled look – what happened to my plaid skirts? He immediately assumes I've become a speed freak. This is amusing; touching amphetamines would cause me to spinout forever. Upon giving me numerous tests, the doctor assures me I am fine, just fine, but I worry too much. And, at this age, when I should be enjoying life, I ought to be a bit calmer . . . He prescribes Valium. After sampling what I suppose to be a placebo, I'm as near tranquil as any hysteric-by-nature can be. Four of them turn a Reality Attack to a mere curiosity piece.

Driving home, feeling mellow, with the past fading behind and the future looming ahead, I try to analyze what's causing my mental state. It must be more than shadows. I have operated under some strange premise that I am unique, destined to do something of significance. I have never exactly known what this great contribution is to be – only that it is fated to happen.

This is all very nice in concept; the only conflict is how I'm going to achieve it. The distant possibility that I will not, after all, marry Jim, has dawned on me. (He is the only man who comes complete with love and money.) I will have to struggle away for years, with no one to support me, with people thinking I'm ill, deluded, trying to come up with a Masterpeice. I might even die alone, anonymous. There will be no mark of my existence here. I probaby won't even get a tombstone. This is quite terrifying, since my mind is particularly gifted in repeating, you'll have to do it alone. Everyone has to do it alone.

I sigh and wish I'd learned to smoke cigarettes. I flick the radio stations, but it all sounds the same. My eyes are burning from the light-to-moderate smog. I wonder why there don't seem to be any famous women artists. A quote from one of my painting teachers blares up at me, "Most women are good in art school, but when they leave, they usually just get married and make their own sculptures." Babies. Women make babies. This all-consuming talent is the reason why they can't be so selfish as to make art, too, or instead. There must be a mistake. After all, humans are prone to err. Once people thought the world was flat and God had a beard.

Reaching the San Diego Freeway, I recall getting rid of that God-with-a-beard image. I was sitting in the backseat of a carload of people. Looking out the window, I had been praying away like mad over some dire need, when suddenly, I must've gotten stuck mid-prayer. All I noticed were swarms of cars, all stuffed with people. And this was just an insignificant Los Angeles freeway.

What if they were praying too? How could God listen to me? He would never have time – even if angels relayed messages, it still wouldn't be fast enough. There would have to be a waiting line! First come, first served. What about the people in Italy, Spain, and France? The possiblity of being heard, with all this international clamor to the skies, was impossible.

Coming back to Sunset Boulevard, I find my thoughts are dimming, losing clarity. I am simply exhausted, and glad to come home to emptiness. I can stare at the walls with no excuses. I have nothing to say, I don't know what we're doing here. I just don't see why there isn't a clinic for Reality Attack victims instead of freeway thinking and Valium doctors . . .

THAT NIGHT I WAKE UP TO HEAR RAIN pouring down in torrents, beating on the roof. There is a preternatural stillness pervading over all. I feel aware in the nervous pit of my stomach. A few minutes later the phone begins to ring. Glancing at the clock, I see it's four A.M. I know it's Jim. My body is strangely immobile, I have no desire to leap out of bed and grab the phone. Though I can see him alone, hurting, I know he'll just make me sicker. The standard ten rings take an eternity to end. In the chill following them, I summon up cynicism. I think, well, now he can just call the next girl on his list. I fall asleep with bitterness and pain, but the next day the sun rises, and the rain is gone.

The next time around I answer, and the voice on the phone is as sexy, sad, and coaxing as ever. My heart chokes in my throat, a revolting characteristic. Oh, my poor baby, and I give way, caught up in my nonsensical dream: this will be the time. The time for what – is hardly clear. I still harbor secret hopes that people really do drift off into Utopia together. Now, when I reach the parking lot, I'm greeted by a sight that comes closer to a modern segment of the Inferno.

Jim's car has some guy's warped body hanging out the front door. His pretzel contortion has caught his lower legs around the gear-shift knob, while his head is on the ground. He's either dead or passed-out. I walk by, wondering if I should at least fold him back up, but his noisy, upside-down breathing scares me and I just tip-toe by.

Jim doesn't look much better than his friend, except he's sitting. Actually, he's slumping. While slumping, he's writing directly on the desk which supports him. He continues scribbling for a few moments, not reacting to my presence, or perhaps oblivious to it. Judging from his ghastly white face and bleary eyes, Jim isn't exactly with it. He does finally catch on to the fact that I'm here. I am staring at a candle made to resemble a cock, and find it in rather poor taste. Of course, no one has lit it.

"Can we go to your house?" Jim's voice rasps out. "Please? I hate it here! I don't want to go to any motels." This causes a shudder of loathing before he goes on. "Won't you take me away to your house?" In his eyes, my house seems to have turned into the Utopia I can't find.

"Sure, come on," I say nervously, hoping he can make it downstairs. "Your friend . . . He looks kind of sick, down there, Jim."

"Babe can take care of himself. He's just fine. Leave him alone!" I am taken aback at his sudden anger, accompanied by resentful, suspicious glances.

"Okay, I just felt sorry for him"

Jim's anger has inspired him to flounce aimlessly

about the room, indignantly picking up various belongings he has scattered around as a drunken stripper.

"Can we go now?" He's an impatient brat, sick and tired of Disneyland.

"Yes, I said."

"I'm so glad we can go to a house!"

I hear him babbling behind me in incoherent spurts as we go to the car. He lapses into relieved silence, and is half asleep when we get to my place. He follows me inside. We march past Kathy, who's feigning sleep, and go to the back. It's a fairly large room, but crammed with wall-to-wall paintings and one rickety cot for emergencies. Jim, the endless emergency, falls down on this as though it were a silken divan. He looks around anxiously, in confusion, grasping for certainty and order, which I can tell doesn't appear. It's pathetic, he should hire a mother. His disorientation calms as I undress him, covering him with blankets and sheets.

A pleased look settles over his face, but suddenly alarmed, he asks, "Aren't you going to lay down with me?"

"Just a second."

I can't imagine where I'll fit, but I take my clothes off anyway. He's abnormally cooperative, helping me find a comfortable position.

"Won't you talk to me? Say anything you want. Flow of consciousness, you know. Anything that comes to your mind. Just talk to me."

"Nothing comes to my mind and I don't know what to . . . "

"Golden. Golden. You're golden!" Jim is hallucinating. His eyes have grown wider, totally taken with my goldenness. I am relieved, I won't have to talk. He weaves my hair around his fingers as he repeats his transfixed vision, "Golden, golden . . . " This harmless image turns him into a silly boy who has a crush on me. He starts to play around with sex just like my second grade boyfriend. Sensual curiosity, not sexual. It's fun.

"What is this?" he asks, pointing to his cock. Now he's really regressing.

"I don't know. Really." He has become obsessed with this strange and new attachment to his body, and regards it abstractly.

"What is it?" he repeats, persistently in his four-year-old voice.

"I think it is real obvious-looking. Primeval," I offer. He's been working on this problem for years; I sure as hell can't solve it.

He temporarily forgets his nameless appendage in favor of pulling me down next to him. Jim rocks me back and forth in a slow, contagious, reassuring motion. It seems especially comforting in the confines of this small space. I can't tell who's the parent and who's the child anymore. It's all a pleasant blur. We're all tied up together.

He buries his head between my breasts and repeats, "I love you, I love you, I love you," over and over, in this small voice, a tiny, touching voice of belief and need. He repeats his words and continues his slight rocking until he falls asleep to the fairy-tale tune he's created. I go along with him.

WHEN WE WAKE LATER, LIGHT IS STREAM-ing through the windows. Kathy has gone and we go back to my bed where we can be noisy without worry. I walk around and pick up clothes to put in the closet, while he sits, in a mild daze, watching me.

Finally, he says, "We've always had an understanding, haven't we?" His expression is sweet and hopeful but I reject it. I am angry he hasn't said one damn word about my paintings, and they're absolutely lining the room, my naked soul – and he makes no comment! I won't keep him happy with lies, the insensitive egomaniac.

"I think I've always understood you. I don't think you understand me." My blunt distortion of his question hangs in the air, and then floats away – somewhere over his head. He looks disappointed and stupefied.

When we get into my bed, he is Jim the man, not Jim the kid. All traces of drunkenness have disappeared. Some of the previous, trusting magic drifts in and around us, though his sensuality has been transfused with plain sex. The only thing spectacular or unusual about it is that it's not spectacular or unusual. We fall asleep again.

When I wake up, I see Jim inspecting the stack of books by my bed.

"Are these all for school? he asks, amazed.

"No. None of them are. They're for me." I say.

He has come upon a William Blake book, and is quoting random blurbs from memory.

"I really love Blake! He's one of my favorite writers," he says ecstatically. "Can I borrow this for a little while? I'm always meaning to go to Pickwick and get it. But I just never get around to it."

He's so excited, I'm touched, saying he can keep it, even though I know I'll have to run out and get another one. It soothes my Reality Attacks as well as Valium, sometimes. For now, this affinity for Blake softens the mood, giving us a bit of luxury and drama to bathe in before dressing for our separate worlds.

Pausing at the door, perched between the division of realities we are soon to depart for, he says, "All good things must come to an end." He gives me a hopeless smile to make up for the corny statement. I want to drag him back into my world, beg him not to leave me, plead that things don't have to end. But I don't. The door opens and closes, and I lock it. We walk away, the heads of a funeral procession.

In my car, the true conversion to reality occurs. Jim stares at me, nothing unusual, but his voice sounds weird and shocked.

"You look radiant! You look like you're in love!" he exclaims.

It echoes over to me, sounding like the sort of excited, but objective remark one would make over a strange, violet-feathered, two-headed bird. It also implies I'm in love with some secret person, not him. It stings to the quick. I look straight ahead. He continues his role of a dumb scientist.

"Maybe it's your make-up. You've changed your make-up. You hardly wear any."

"No." I shake my head, smiling wickedly at his meaningless remark.

"I think it must be that all you wear is mascara now. You just look radiant, really!"

I almost choke. If they could make a mascara that produced love radiance they'd make millions. He continues dissecting, tearing cruelly at my face, digging fruitlessly for the cause of my damn radiance, which must be slaughtered by now.

"I guess I just feel better about things. Better than I used to. So maybe I look better." The person who said this was lying. Lying for survival.

"I wish I could mellow out. I keep thinking I'll have to. Have some peace of mind." His voice is hollow with sincerity and longing.

Despite myself, despite the fact that he doesn't know love when it's staring him in the face, I begin to feel for him again.

"I just hope I don't get some long disease like cancer," Jim rolls his eyes upward. "Spare me from cancer!" Then he gets instense and scary saying, "Sometimes I call you because I'm afraid I'm going to die alone." This must've come out stronger than he had intended, he attempts to lighten it by adding, "I want someone to write down all the things I say while I'm dying." Evidently, he thinks he may come out with the universal secrets and I nod.

Suddenly, the car is in front of his office, the threshold of his world, it has happened too fast. We sit there, saying nothing, just looking. There's an unfinished feeling in the air. He reaches over and hugs me. Then he sits back again, probing, searching my eyes, as if whatever's missing is inside them. After a long, baffled pause, he gets out of the car. He just stands there, though. I know he's afflicted with the same incompleteness as I. He looks awkward and unsure. More long searching. Inside, part of me understands: He is looking for confirmation. I refuse to acknowledge it, as he says, "Goodbye, I'll call you tonight."

Backwards, from his vision, I see the girl in the car fading. And he regains cool control. Oh, stubborn egos, hurt pride, why can't I say, I love you? He remembers who he is, why he's there and walks away. My face sets. My car manages to back itself expertly off. I feel he's watching me, and I have to look at him again. Now he's caught me in his eyes, faltering and lost for this instant, asking why. I manage to semi-smile, semi-wave a semi-goodbye. My being is a semi-real involvement; I have to leave before I lose my mind.

CHAPTER 17

NOT TO TOUCH
THE EARTH

ONE NIGHT, WHILE IMAGINING ANOTHER land guarded by misty, swaying vines, made up of glass castles, and inhabited by opalescent-eyed people who dance liquidly through light forests, I put on a purple velvet dress and walk barefoot, out into the rain. Here, under the spell I have cast upon myself, I am fully under my Sybil Witch-Goddess dreams. I'm a new, magic creature, and I must go tell Jim I love him before the trance wears off, and I turn into a person of fear again. I drive down the wet, neon streets, the reflective color washes of rain illuminating and soothing the hard edges of my mind.

When I reach the office, I see his car in the parking lot. I leap out – a rabbit into pure space. When I touch the ground, my eyes fall upon a girl in a long dress. She's just standing there, staring at me. Though she has a strange, stately quality I immediately respond to, I can't understand why I feel I should run up and hug her like a dear, loved and missed relative. I restrain myself, thinking this is a *stranger* in a parking lot. She waits as I approach her, smiling before I say, "Where's Jim?"

"Away." She makes her words long and dramatic. Her nearly emaciated arms move fluidly through the air, demonstrating his away-ness. She gives me a concerned look, then firmly states, "You need some water!" I regard her skeptically. "The way you just flew out of your car, you might have never landed!" She laughs, then says, "I'm Jim's sister. It's lucky that I'm here now to help you. I'll take you over to the Clear Thoughts Building. It has good water." She laughs again, as if to reassure me. "You should have seen yourself! You're going much too fast. Come on."

"All right, I guess it's true," I laugh, half-heartedly. I don't really want to go there, I'll have to see Pam's shop, Themis, which I'm sure Jim named. I prefer ignoring the bond it represents between them. But, taken in by this girl's hospitality and desire to cure me by means of water, I figure I can risk it. She looks me up and down and stops with approval at my bare feet. She, too, is shoeless.

"You should always go barefoot in the city," she nods. "You have to keep in contact with yourself and the ground."

"It's cement."

"Well, usually. Whenever you see real ground, walk on it instead."

"But people don't like it," I lament, referring both to the ground and bare feet.

"That doesn't matter." We have reached the drinking fountain unharmed, and I'm actually in a fairly good mood. She supervises my water drinking.

"Everything is based on water. We come from the sea. It works better than any drug. Always. It will always cure you, it's not like other things." I nod agreement with her, while sneaking three Valiums in my mouth. "You really have to calm down, you're almost panting!"

"I know."

"Jim and I are the illegitimate children of Ingrid Bergman and Orson Welles." She says this in a secretive, lowered tone. I try to arrange my face properly for the occasion. "We were separated when we were very young. It was a scandal, expecially because we were always trying to make love!"

"Oh. Really?" I want to sound unalarmed, take it in stride that I'm alone, in a dark, deserted building with her.

"Yes. But sometimes Jim forgets. It was such a long time ago." She smiles again. "You'd better drink some more water, you need a lot."

"Uh huh," I agree readily, gulping mouthfuls.

"Now that I've returned to my rightful place," she continues, "we'll get married. But first, we have to solve the incest law. People have this legal thing about incest! It's *so* ridiculous. We love each other! They don't want us to get married." This troubles her to the extent that she stops talking.

"My girlfriend, she really loved her brother, too," I offer. I have to offer something to the deafening silence. "It was kind of weird, I guess, but he was just a step-brother, so I guess it's different."

"What about Pam?" I ask her.

"Oh, *Pam!*" She waves this away, too. "Pam and Jim helped each other through a lot of hard times when they didn't have anyone to love. But that's over now. Pam's in love with Ned, the co-owner of Themis, anyway."

"I thought she was devoted to Jim!" I gasp, stupified, all my mental images disintegrating.

"No. It was just security. For both of them." I can tell

the subject is beginning to bore her as we walk back down the stairway. "What do they call you?" she demands.

"Judy."

"I am Joanna." This at least saves me from some formal blunder of name asking.

BACK AT THE OFFICE, SHE WANTS TO SIT down in this little, muddy garden instead of going upstairs. I still secretly think Jim is up there and will soon hear our voices, and thus, come down and save me, so I go along with her. "The earth people are trying to take us over. We'll have to be very careful," she informs me.

"That's true," I sigh. They've been trying to take me over for years.

"I spotted you as a water person right away. There aren't many left, you know. They always look like ancient, aristocratic statues. We both look that way, have you noticed?"

In the half-light it seems as though our faces do bear a resemblance, in a half-angelic, half-satanic, no time sense.

"It's funny they don't recognize us," I reply, wondering if insanity is catching.

"They will." She quickly switches on her oddly formulated views, a mixture of world mythologies turned into one, now her's. She's quite intelligent to have made such a brew, really. We laugh about the lemmings who never really drowned, and the earth people, who're so obsessed with their serious living.

The light breeziness begins to drag when she says, "Soon, our place as true leaders will be given back to us. We have the true origins of life behind us. We are going to start a new race."

"How?"

"It will start when Jim and I are married and walk into the sea. Others will follow. Who are not afraid, who believe."

I'm getting doubtful. She isn't quite as flexible with fantasy as I'd hoped. She almost takes things as literally as those madmen who once arrested me. She senses my lack of conviction. "Do you know that Jim loves me so much, he said he would sacrifice his *bridge* for me?" This, I assume, is her name for his great male genitals.

"Jim said that?" I find it next to impossible that Jim would ever do such a thing for anyone, even if his life depended on it.

"Yes." She holds her face up, hopefully. "Don't you think we look alike?" she half pleads.

"Yeah, I do," I lie.

"Jim has so much trouble remembering our past! I'm really having problems with him. He is so *attached* to being an earth person sometimes. You wouldn't think so, would you? But that's why he has problems with his memory. I know he's just scared." She pauses unhappily. "His parents, the ones that took him after we split up, they didn't love him. I asked how much his father loved him, and he made a little space between his thumb and forefinger." She illustrates this gesture. "I asked how much his mother loved him, and he . . . " She widens the gap a bit more. "Isn't that sad? He couldn't even talk about it!"

I sense her compassion, and do feel it's sad. I feel tired and over-exposed, like a piece of film left in the sun to burn. She looks at me and says, "It's too bad you don't have a soul mate, too. It's too bad Bryan Jones is dead, he would've been perfect for you. Maybe Charlie Watts, you have the same lionish coloring."

I shake my head no. As long as she's taken Jim, and is about to castrate and drown him while she gives out English rock stars to console me, at least she could wave her wand at Mick Jagger. She has been interesting company, but now I want to go home. I don't know how to tell her without offending her. Though her antennae are crossed, she picks up on things pretty well.

"I have this crazy ex-lover. He's been following me all across the country and everything. Ever since I was released from The Institution." She stops and looks angry. I squirm uncomfortably. "You know, there was a girl just like you there. She didn't have a soul mate either, but at least she made sense. But anyway, he just won't stop following me. Now he's staying across the street. So he can watch me."

"Across the street?"

"Yes." She's off-hand about it. "He says he's going to assassinate Jim, and then me. He's just *so* jealous, he won't give up. You'd better be careful though, he may mistake you for one of us and hit you. He's dangerous. I wish he'd leave me alone."

"Yeah, well, I'd better go then."

She doesn't react to this, too busy thinking about her ex-lover, I guess. I say goodbye and flee. All water soothing has worn off, I drive off to my stodgy reality feeling stupid, and clumsy, a regular earth person. I envy her freedom, her fleeting mania; she is really on to something – just a little *too* on for me.

CHAPTER 18

SHAMAN'S BLUES

AFTER THIS FLEETING ACQUAINTANCE, I take a few steps back. Going off that far edge looks too easy for comfort, there seem to be many drawbacks. I feel it would be smarter to make a plea for sanity. I'm not ready for the sea. But when Jim calls me the next week, I'm certainly nuts enough to accept his rescue-me-from-deathly-solitude request. The moment I arrive, he jumps into the car in a complete get-me-out-of-this-place frenzy. He wants me to take him to the Alta Cienega Motel. It's only half a block away, but I guess he couldn't get there unchaperoned. I haven't been there since the beginning.

It's rush hour for work people, La Cienega is overflowing with them, and naturally, under Jim's great influence, I'm busy making an illegal left-hand turn. A woman nearly crashes into us, then honks, screams inarticulately and waves her arms wildly at us. Jim smiles politely at her. Then he turns to me, grinning with childish wisdom. "Pretend your car is broken," he says.

I can't help but laugh and turn into the driveway. It's

still too steep. Getting out and walking up to his room brings on a mild Reality Attack from déjà-vu flashes.

He stops, and posing as the innocent, says, "Oh, you've never been here with me. Have you?" I go blank, breathing is difficult, especially when you aren't a compassionate woman who just laughs at the stupid things he does.

Once inside, he becomes intensely somber. "I met this guy last night. He wants me to act in a film he's making."

"What's it about?" I ask.

"There's this band of wild, hashish-smoking children, wandering around in a Moroccan dessert. I would lead them."

"Oh." It sounds a bit weird to me. "I think you ought to be careful about what you're in."

"This guy seemed pretty together," he shakes his head defensively. "I want to get more involved with film, somehow. At least I'd like to write some screenplays."

"Yeah, I like the way you write, only," the words spill out of me, unaware, "why is it so morbid?"

"I write about sex and death. And if you think that's *morbid*, well . . . " He gives me a look of icy revulsion.

"Well, that line – about pulling your eyes out!"

"That," the adult explains, "is about a contemporary issue. SMOG!" I see he does not care for criticism.

"I liked the part, about being metamorphosized from a mad dancing body on hillsides to . . . "

"To a pair of eyes staring in the dark," he finishes for me, his anger forgotten.

"I had to tear out your dedication. 'To Pamela Susan'," I confess. "I even made a collage out of it. Something about fallen birds and ink stains."

"I felt I owed it to her." The diplomat minimizes bonds, showing no particular allegiance, but harmony, self-harmony.

"I went into her shop one day. It was nice."

My penchant for confession is going too far and I stop, merely thinking out the rest of the scene. Pam had walked in, seen the Japanese silk dress I was wearing, and clutched at it, her huge blue eyes hypnotized.

"You just never see things like this anymore! It's so beautiful!" She forgot to let go of the material and began staring at me. Kathy was with me and sensing a catatonic collapse on my part, found a quick excuse for us to exit. She assured me Pam was just stoned on something, it had nothing to do with remembering my face. I split my last piece of gum backstage with her four years earlier. No, I just knew who she was.

"I don't think she knows who you are." A profound synopsis. "Pam is a good nest builder," Jim explains, adding, "she's a Capricorn." This is supposed to sum her up, I guess. I don't know what it means. "She's just so *vulnerable* about everything." His complaining voice is taking reign.

"I thought vulnerability was good, I mean, you at least *feel*," I answer.

"No. She's too vulnerable. There's a difference." He's insistent. "Besides, we're both egomaniacs. It can never work out." I can't think of any intelligent quips on egomania so I just sit there, a big soppy mess, listening. "I'm usually with older women, anyway." This seems to make no impression on either of us.

"Are they really that different? All the women?" It seems so futile running around with myriad varieties of women, never to really touch any of them. "It seems like it'd get boring or something."

"Yeah. They're all pretty much the same. I don't know why I do it." He sighs, full of quick and heavy depression. "You know, I just think we're all *slaves* to our bodies!"

He glances around, annoyed and uptight. "I say 'you know' too often. I wish I would stop it. I can't stand it when other people do it! And I'm always saying it."

"I have some Valium with me. I think we should take some and just relax," I say.

"Really? I like Valium."

"Yeah," I grimace, "I probably have a life long prescription for them. I get these alienation-from-everything feelings so I have to take them."

"Oh," he looks wary, as if I'd admitted a contagious disease. "That's a bad one." He practically grabs my four offered pills from my hand and swallows them down, the great erasers for lashing minds.

"There was this young girl," Jim begins. "I was with her one night in Hawaii. We didn't talk or anything. But it was just so refreshing, like a spring bath. I'll never forget it. I don't even know who she was."

"I met this girl. Joanna, I think her name was. She was sort of crazy." I remember she might actually be his sister, and stop all following comments.

"Sort of crazy? She was *really* crazy! Not even good crazy!" He flinches.

"She was all right for a night."

"*No*! I was afraid she'd do something to me!"

"Oh, yeah."

"You know, I just discovered that men and women are really different!" He lets this out as a confidence of monumental importance. "I had just always *assumed* that they were alike. I mean men and women. And they aren't. We don't even *see* things the same!" This really blows Jim's mind, and he turns anxiously towards me, his face a ruined jigsaw puzzle, asking, "What do *you* think about that?"

"I'm not really sure. I can see it both ways." My

noncommital answer causes his face to fall apart even more, a picture of confusion. He must be having an identity crisis over the sexes. I don't want to tell him he's the most female male I've ever encountered. "Well, I guess there has to be a difference. Otherwise there'd be just one sex instead of two," I assure him.

I giggle at my words and the slurred, loose way they fall out. The Valium is beginning to take effect, and I feel the tenseness of life easing.

"You know," Jim drawls, "We've known each other for three and a half years now!" I've never figured this out, I'm too bad with numbers, so the extra half year seems particularly astute – he has computed it exactly.

"That's true," I mumble, pleased, as he reaches over for me.

For the first time we feel like two, actual human beings, flesh an blood beings making love without any stories, theatrics, yelling or lies. It is real. Here, isolated in a strange motel room, with the cars honking, the ambulances screaming, the world's gears endlessly grinding away, we're alive, together. Humans being.

IN THIS TRUTH A STRONG POIGNANCY lingers, lasts heavily in the atmosphere. It is acid raw, biting, undisguised, this realness. It admits all things never said but always known. In this fleeting grace, identities are gone, and the only love ever felt surfaces, brave, scared, untarnished and pure. Maybe the poignancy is this. In a world of fucking, fucking, fucking with a clothed soul and a fear-studded emotional core, perhaps making love is the ultimate hope (and paranoia). You can be a fish, stripped clean.

We get up, after laying in the aftermath of the

unknown, to take a shower. Going back to the bed, we turn on an old Cary Grant movie. We lay back to collapse in sensual histrionics. The characters are just delirious, crazy, with unfounded jealousy and accusations.

"They just don't know about Cosmic Consciousness!" Jim blurts out, gleefully. "But this is a very sophisticated comedy, you know?"

"Yeah, but are you married or not? Lately everyone tells me you're married. All the time. They think I'm real dumb."

"Those people don't know what they're talking about," he says scornfully. "You just have to ignore them. I'm much too young and irresponsible to get married, anyway!"

"I didn't think so."

We erase the world, its words, movies, lies and truths for a little longer, then he decides it's time to get dressed and go to work. First, he says he knows a good place we can have breakfast, or whatever meal his time schedule deems it's time for. I dress, too. Jim has to stop and watch me, fascinated.

"You're really *big,* you know?"

"Big? What do you mean, big? Do you mean fat?"

"No. I mean just big. Big like Ursula Andress or Britt Eklund, or something. That kind of big."

"Oh, okay." My ego is almost soothed.

"You really ought to be a model, you'd really be a good model." My muscles tense in fury, here I am, not fat, but worse, typecast as The Body.

"I want to be an *artist!*" I nearly scream. He ignores my outburst.

"Do the men in the street always whistle at you?"

"Only the *idiots!*" I turn around, feeling ill. He ignores this, too, beginning to whistle some stupid tune himself.

He keeps this up as we walk outside and down the stairs to my car. An awkward, off-balance quality is in the air. I sense I should have walked over to his side of the car rather than mine. It's too late to retrace my steps, say, hey let's do that whole scene over – please?

"I'm not really hungry anymore. I think I'll just walk across the street now. Is that all right?"

"Yeah, I'm not hungry, either." I am disappointed.

"I love you," he says over the roof.

"I love you, too." I echo over the tin. It sounds hollow; I walk over to his side.

He looks and feels oddly hard and solemn. I'm quiet, trying to fathom the play of his features. He looks at me strangely.

"I called you, a week or so ago. In the afternoon. I guess you were at school. Your mother or someone answered." He sounds hesitant.

"Yeah, my mother, she was visiting."

"Well, she asked if you should call me at the *studio*! Who was she talking about? Do you know someone who has a studio? I mean, she must've thought I was someone else. Some artist with a studio." He ends it lamely, dead, in the air.

I am stricken, fumbling helplessly with his way of turning situations upside down and backwards. I hear myself trying to explain it was semantics, office and studio mean the same thing to her. But I can't bridge the gap he has created, he overcomes my strength. My explanations are not heard, he's not listening to me.

"I'll call you," he nods and smiles as my heart sinks, and I think, please don't drag it into the mud of promises. When you call again, I'll come back. So let's drop it, drop it with tomorrows. I smile back at him. I am learning to be phony. I drive away.

A few moments later, at the signal, I see him again. The man with such audacious self-confidence takes his facile show so seriously at times it means all to him, until he falls. From a distance, I watch him in sadness. Because he dies a little bit too much each time he falls, he falls a little too hard, too fast. His shell grows more brittle as his insides hurt more, believe less. Watching Jim walk his walk, the way he walks alone, the impact of his aloneness hits me. The man is solitary. Forever solitary.

CHAPTER 19

L.A. WOMAN

IN EARLY OCTOBER, JIM'S VOICE ON THE other end of the line is broken and thick. "I just got back from Miami. Won't you come and see me?"

"Where are you?" Thinking is no longer one of my basic functions.

"Uh, it's the Gene Autrey Hotel, you know, the one on the corner. On Sunset. You'll see it. It's there."

"What room?" I scribble down his details on a box of slides that've just been taken of my work. "Okay, I'll see you in a while."

"Wear something long and flowing, so you'll look like part of The Procession." This last command sinks in slowly as I hang up the phone.

Soon, I'm in a gas station asking the attendant if he's heard of any Gene Autry Hotels. He is nice, it's early in the morning to be getting such questions.

"It must be The Continental Hyatt House – just down the street. I think that used to be it," he says.

"Thanks." I actually smile at the guy.

"No trouble," he smiles back.

The air looks dead from the grey overcoat of leftover smog and smoke. The consuming blaze of this autumn's fire has left a world of ash, a feeling of bleak destruction. It looks as though L.A. is coming to an end. The Continental Hyatt House is no less sinister and austere viewed through this smudged morning twilight. The moment I arrive, a uniformed man takes my car away, placing a ticket in my hand. I walk inside.

An elevator is waiting to confront me. It has unfathomable colored buttons in meticulous lines. I am supposed to push one. I can get out of some foreign cars, open some modern refrigerator doors, now I'm pushing a colored button, listening to a jolt and entering an elevator. I have mastered another feat. I arrive, intact, on the right floor, and I haven't broken a thing yet. I realize I'm knocking on some man's hotel room door. He opens it a suspicious crack, deems me safe and lets me in.

Jim stands on the other side, naked as usual, and looking tragic as hell. I must've forgotten, that is Jim, and Jim is that. His face looks drained of feeling.

I glance around this hollow suite his body now occupies – the sterile luxury, the empty space, filled only by two quarts of vodka, one empty, sitting side-by-side next to some white powder. And, of course, the telephone. He has that, too, along with the incongruous orange juice.

"I just got back from Miami," he says, as if that's all he knows, his explanation for being.

"Was it awful?" I don't know many details about his trial in Miami, I just know he and the law can't possibly mix. "I mean, all the bullshit. Legal games. Money for freedom . . . " I trail off, feeling inappropriate as he makes a meaningless gesture and dismisses further discussion of this subject by putting a wall over his face.

He wants no questions, no reminders of something he refuses to acknowledge himself. A dagger edges into my numb confusion. I thought he was a soldier for truth and guts, no matter how offensive, but now it seems pretense has become his muse. The one who laughed at The Game as a game is shaken and defeated, the one who protested against escape has taken it.

I don't know what to do, I don't know what to say. I'm fearful that the sullen atmosphere will take solid shape and attack me. I sit on the edge of the bed and smile tentatively, looking at his face, feeling it still hit me. I take off my sandals and watch his wall soften into amiability.

"Make yourself at home," he says, a little too suggestively. I take off the rest of my clothes and relief spreads fully over his countenance. A smile appears. He wants dreams, gentle lies, he wants to forget and needs tenderness. He does not care to talk and I know no better but to comply. He brings over a bag of coke and we use some.

"Do you want a drink?" he asks.

"No thanks, not now."

"Let's go outside, okay?"

"Yeah, all right."

The wonders of coke have smoothed both of us. We walk out to the balcony, wordless and serene. We lean out over the railing, naked virgins, pure and innocent, washed clean. We watch the deluge of honking cars, lost, but still driving on through the tainted brown air so far below. Oh, yeah, those are people down there, people in the smog, smoke and ashes, people. I lean back, suddenly totally unable to take the view and feel his arms softly surround me. After silent tears thinking, we're children, God, save us, I turn around to Jim, for his eyes, now sweet and kind, the harsh cruelty lost. He holds me back, a crystal figurine, a fragile figment.

"You're beautiful."

"You are too." I answer, swirling and rising while he kisses me in this glass netherland of forevers.

Everything is good. Resolved, his arm around me, protecting us both, we walk back into the room, transformed. Laying on the bed, feeling his warmth, slow euphoria rises up between us.

Feeling takes us away, only to lose hold, give way, unwind, and crash us down, way down. Jim's lost it. I open my eyes, startled, taken off-balance by such a ruthless crash. I focus on his face in confusion.

"Let's have some more coke," he suggests, acting unshattered. "It will at least numb our nostrils."

AS HE CROSSES THE ROOM, I LOOK EVENLY at his body, a body once molded with such delicate beauty, whole and fine. I see it's going under, careless abuse hasn't come unheeded. Maybe it would be easier to accept on a less well-made, graceless breed, but he seems a loused up thoroughbred neglected, forgotten, misused.

"Your stomach, it's getting out of proportion to the rest of your body." I hope this sounds like a mild warning to cool it.

"Please don't say those terrible things to me! Are you going to do that again?" He looks frightened, wounded, hostile.

"I've never said any *terrible things* to you! Stop being such a martyr! I mean, you're really getting into that tragic hero trip." I hear my words ring back hard, unmerciful, and look down.

"Promise you'll never say any more bad things to me," he pleads.

"I promise," I sigh, wondering what I *can* say.

The phone rings, interrupting whatever atrocity I might next commit. I quickly gather it's a girl who talks a lot. I begin getting bored and angry so I glare at him. He responds to this nonverbally, handing me the phone and putting his finger to his lips. I listen, at first fascinated, to this girl's breathless, breakneck rampage.

"I have a job here! I can't leave! What am I supposed to do? I live here! I have to *work*! I just can't leave! *Jim*?"

I hand the phone back to him, frantic. "Uh huh, yeah, oh," Jim says, before handing it back to me.

The originality of listening to one of his nationally hysterical girlfriends is wearing off. I throw the phone back at him and stalk across the room to glare unimpeded. This finishes the conversation for him, too. He hangs up and walks over to me, pleased with himself.

"What was *she* like?" I ask impassively.

"She had long red hair. Straight down her back."

He kisses my neck, his explanations sting with brutality. I walk away and sit down, uptight.

"Are you married or not? I don't care! I just get sick of being contradicted. Everyone that thinks they know you or Pam insists that you're married. I'm not kidding!"

"Pam is just this crazy girl I went with once. Now she thinks we're married." He waves it off. "But you take even the most mystical chick, and mention marriage . . . "

His point seems to end here, leaving the effect of marriage on even the most mystical chicks spread across his disgusted face. It looks as though Jim's having a fine time dismissing everything in existence, getting down to the bone of killing.

"Do you want to look at my slides?"

"Yeah, let me see them."

"Well, you have to hold them up to the light."

He crosses the room and sits down by a lamp. However, this does not enable his mind to focus. It's clouded with miles of fog. When he reaches one painting I did more under his influence than mine, he doesn't even notice. Anyone who was able to read and hear what his images evoked could've seen the blatant similarity. It's all in muted warm and cool shades of pale yellow, the differences blocking out a highway leading to a desert horizon. Above this, there's a moon, and at the highway's edge, stretched like a shoreline, a row of symbols: fish skeletons, round arrows, sun signs underlined, parts of an alternate language. I'm stunned when he just passes it by.

"I want a drink," I state firmly. "Let's not look at anymore of these! You can't *see* them." He looks puzzled, hands me my vodka and orange juice. I drink it down like so much soda-pop and say, as morosely as possible, "Can I have another, please?"

"I'm out of orange juice. I could send out for some. I should have some."

"Straight."

"Okay." Jim gives me an odd glance. He has never seen my self-destructive powers unleashed. It must be out of my virgin-whore character. All I want to do is get drunk and snort as much coke as possible. Jim decides the fitting thing for him to do, in his violent boredom, is piss in the empy vodka bottle. He does it looking on, abstracted. I watch this equally abstracted, vaguely feeling it's an absurd performance. Then he makes a wild attempt to fuck me. It doesn't work again. This time I don't feel like the understanding lover.

"Is there something wrong with me? Am I doing something wrong or something? Am I repulsive?"

I already feel *bad enough*! Don't make me feel worse!" Jim's bluesy whine is upstaged by hostility.

"All right!" I pounce off the bed, grab the bottle, and lock myself in the bathroom. I look at myself in the mirror. I'm definitely *not* repulsive, there's something wrong with him after all. After an adequate sulking period, I walk out, drunker, dumber and more defiant.

"Will you put on those sandals? And walk around the room?" he immediately asks.

"I guess so."

It sounds pretty stupid, but there's nothing else happening. I begrudgingly think this may placate his lousy black mood. Only when I stand do I realize this is a plot to make me look asinine. I'm going to look like a poster for horny men. My face sets haughtily at this, even though I follow his pointless directions. It feels like an audition for basic walking-in-front-of-a-maniac.

"Stand on that chair!" he orders, suddenly. The harsh note in his voice causes actual fear in me, mingled with a strong flash that we're engaged in some ugly ego contest. How far will I go? How far can I go? Is it submissive love or self-abhorrence? I obey, as nastily as possible. I stand on the chair, lean one hip out in contempt at both our roles, and stare, unflinching, into his eyes. He's not in the least satisfied with my airs. "Turn around!" I turn. "Bend over!"

Summoning up my full coordination and resources of grace, I lightly slip off both sandals, and throw them at him. I step down from the chair.

"I *hate* you!" This scathing remark comes out very well. There can be no mistake in pronunciation. It has no effect. I fling my body violently across the bed and look away. There is nothing, just silence.

"Well, now what are we going to do?" I ask, my voice full of disdain.

"Play Monopoly," he hisses back.

So, this is incompatibility: the desire to mentally mutilate, or if you're lucky, permanently cripple the one beside you. I bury my head into a pillow, wanting to burrow myself away, bury my growing apathy. The phone rings again. Through the muffles, I hear him say, "Call me back later. I'm asleep." He must be making a stack of friends. I hear him ask for a room number and have a conversation concerning the absurdity of big weddings with his old friend, Babe, the human pretzel. They have a pretty slick Vaudeville phone act down, and Jim is revived.

"I could take this belt," he holds up a leather belt, "and just sort of flick you on the ass with it," he says, giving me another bit of cocaine, sweet cocaine.

"I don't *like* pain!"

"It doesn't hurt. It just sensitizes your nerve endings. It really doesn't hurt. I wouldn't do it hard."

"I'm not some kind of physical masochist!"

"You mean you won't even try it?" he taunts.

"Okay, but you'd better not hurt me."

He makes three light flicks over my body. Although it doesn't hurt, it also doesn't do a thing for my nerve endings. Aside from that, I don't much like the look in his eyes.

Animal cunning is coming to me as I slowly, nonchalantly turn over and say, "I think it's boring. I mean, unless you're really *into* pain and being whipped. It just isn't interesting." He looks disappointed and sits down to pout with his useless belt.

A FEW MOMENTS LATER, THE OTHER redhead saves the day again. Persistent girl, she can have him, complete with stage directions and belts. I can only guess her words from his.

"I don't know, I don't know *what* will happen. They haven't decided. Do you love me? I don't know. When I'm in jail, you can bring me chocolate chip cookies and I will write all the time. It won't be bad."

I walk away to put on my clothes. I see him watching me, catching my attention with a hand gesture. He says, "I love you" to her, then, sure he's got me full face, *winks*. Winks like we're partners in sickness.

All I can think is it could be me on the other end of that line. He doesn't love anyone, just like he believes no one can love him. He can only hurt, the way he thinks others hurt him; he can only mock and hate, the way he mocks and hates himself. I want to get the hell away from him and all the years. Away. I reach for my purse, and smooth down my clothes and hair.

He hangs up. His eyes are nothing but personal anguish. How can you leave, how can you leave me? This expression of his brings on a strong, insane reaction inside me. Surging, I turn evil.

I slip down to his side, first caress and kiss his head, then move down for a full scale attack over his body, moaning softly, acting overcome with lust. I do everything I know that will make him lose control. I want to make him crazy, I want to make him come – to have that final power over him. I hate him. This is the only way I can win, take over his impotence, drinking, women, lies, and bullshit, force him to forget all the damn pain he holds like a flag. When he comes inside me, I feel a moment of malicious victory. But it doesn't last. My original plan of immediately leaving backfires. An awful, unearthly cry comes tearing out of me, welling up and over.

My tears slip out, brim over into unbridled hysteria. I don't care what he thinks, don't give a damn for his precious ego any longer. I sit up with a jagged, brutal movement, pushing him away, crying, half screaming, mumbling to him, at him.

"I hate you, I hate you! I *love* you, why can't you see I love you? I've always loved you, all this time, and you never see, never see. You can't. You don't care. I hate you, hate you. You've never even seen me – seen who I am. I never want to see you again! Why can't you see I love you?" This tumbles out, past its time, in chaos and vehemence before I lapse back into tears.

After a while, I come to, enough to realize my head is buried in his chest. I wonder how long it's been there? I wonder if he's heard anything I've said? I look up at him.

His face looks as caved-in, wrecked, and dismembered as his voice choking out a plea, "Judy, please don't. I can't stand to see you like this. I'm going to just keep crying too. Please, can't you stop? I can't *stand* to see you cry like this."

In my ears, Jim has assumed a paternal voice, telling me how to behave, and more rage takes over. I stop flat, outright. I look coldly at this person I once endowed with all holy qualities. Though his eyes are filled with tears and sorrow, I no longer know why.

"I'm sorry," he says, "I know I've been unfeeling."

For a moment, and forever, I reach over to understand

him once more, understanding that selfishness that makes him blind to how he's affecting others, that self-obsession that will always be unconscious, driving him. He does not drive himself. The part of him that wounds and destroys others is the weakness within him that wounds and destroys himself more. With the blade turned inward as he pushes against the world, the world pushes the blade in deeper, embedded in his heart as he strikes out, and each time he draws more blood, his own. He's a man caught in quicksand who persists in moving, a man intent on making waves that will only swallow him.

"How old are you?" he asks suddenly, ruining my train of thought. I start at the irrevlevance of such a question, and do not answer. His motivation escapes me.

"Twenty-four?" I stare at him, and shake my head. "Twenty-three?" I shake my head again, feeling my anger grow again. He's beginning to sound incredulous though he's known my age off and on for years. "Twenty-two?"

"No."

"Twenty-one?" I finally nod.

Yes, I am twenty-one. I'm a child, a baby, green. That's why I can't handle these things. That's the problem. Give me a few years and I'll swallow deceit, I'll take lies in love, killing dreams by calculated purpose, hurt and the rest like a bouquet of everlasting roses. It's just my age now, my age. I smile feebly, get up, smooth down my hair and clothes for good, and walk to the door, speechless.

Jim follows me, taking my hand. He wants to restore the romance now, he doesn't want me leaving bitter, of all the insanity in the world. He wants me to now be that untouched princess who thinks life is sweet.

"I promise you I'll call as soon as John's wedding is over today. Probably late in the afternoon. We can go to the movies. All right?"

"Uhm hmn." I nod, looking at the naked man standing in the door.

"You look like a pioneer woman," he smiles.

"Yeah, I'll see you." He kisses me goodbye, and the door shuts. Final.

CHAPTER 20

COMING BACK TO ME

I MOVE TO A GUEST HOUSE IN THE Hollywood Hills. It's down a long, dirt lane, lined with trees and the city's left-over rambling green. I like the way the earth crunches under my car wheels, and I like the huge sunflowers, bent over, looking in my window, past the calico curtains. At night, with the antique lamps turned off, I see the city stretched below me anew, sparkling, multi-colored jewels, softly beckoning. This is my sanctuary, my first place of peace. I retreat to quiet, or music, write poems and make cheese and vegetable casseroles. Here, I'm a secret hippie on a hill after playing feminist-artist in the daily world. I think of Jim, often, but I can only place him in the past or future. I can't imagine him in my present, though I can't deny a strong hope, for later.

Winter has taken its fluid California turn into spring, when I hear Jim has left Los Angeles for France. Rock hasn't worn well, he wants to write, lose his sex-symbol image, be taken seriously. The murmurs I hear sound like doctors giving him a fifty-fifty chance. They're scales of doubt and hope, but my meter's all off; I assume he'll put the pieces back together. When he returns in September, full of decisions on how to reconduct his life, I'll tell him one way to start is by giving me an elaborate apology (for having wasted so much of my time and almost ruining my life). Until then, I can wait.

The phone rings at three A.M. one morning in July. I think it must be Jim, he's returned from Paris early — no one else calls that late. I let the phone ring long enough to gather the composure I'm surprised to have lost so easily. My other symptoms: wildly beating heart, difficulty swallowing, breathlessness, have all returned, thoughtlessly. I'm disappointed in myself, really, after all this time.

"Hello?" I hear the static of long distance wires, then a voice.

"Judy?"

"Yes, who's this?"

"Greg." Greg is a friend, Kathy's old boyfriend.

"Oh." I'm brutally disappointed, even more ashamed of my symptoms showing. "Where are you? The phone sounds weird."

"New York, I'm in New York. It's hot. The time is different here. Have you heard about Jim?"

My mind blanks and swims, dizzy and sick, there's only one thing to hear about Jim, I've heard everything possible and impossible a thousand times before.

"He's dead . . . " My words are no question, they're a muffled, terror-stricken pronouncement. I wait in horror for contradiction. The pause lasts too long, way too long. Greg might as well hang-up now.

"Yes."

"You're drunk. You're drunk, aren't you?"

"Yeah. I've been drunk all night, ever since I found out. And now it's hot already. I feel terrible. I kept thinking someone should tell you, before you woke up to the media. I felt close to him, you know . . . " He trails off into incoherent ramblings while my body oozes out of itself, an overturned bottle.

"I think it's a lousy joke. It's cruel. It's not a very funny way to test my reactions. You know I'm not over him."

"Judy, it's true. It's true." Now he's turned into an "it's true" echo chamber. My mind feels bolted in dumb refusal, lightning rods chain it, hollow stakes ground it. "There's some story about how he and a friend were walking around Père Lachaise, the cemetery, just a few days before, talking about it being a nice place to be buried. There was something about him picking a plot for himself. Like he knew. I think he knew."

"Greg!" This sounds morbidly obscene.

"I don't know if it's true. It's just a story."

"Is Jim dead or not?"

"Jim is dead. What do you think I'm calling for?"

"I don't see how. What did he die from? He couldn't have OD'd. How did he die?"

"Natural causes."

"Natural causes!"

"Something about a blood clot in his heart."

"I don't believe it! And if you're not careful, the same thing will happen to you. You'd better stop drinking Greg, I'm not kidding. You drink too much and you think it's poetic and see what it does. It kills you, and I don't think this is very funny. Is this some kind of joke? He's probably just making a documentary on his death." I begin to laugh.

"He's dead." Greg is unbearably stubborn just because he's another poet who wants to be a film maker.

"If you don't stop drinking, you're gonna kill yourself, you know. The same thing, it's gonna happen, if you're not careful."

"I know. I'm drunk. That's why."

"I don't believe it. Just a minute." I hold the phone away, then cover it. I concentrate on the air. I can't feel that Jim's energy is gone. The air hasn't changed essence. "Greg? I don't think he's dead. I don't sense a loss of his presence. I can't feel it. At least he's not dead in California."

"Are you all right?"

"Yeah. I'm all right!"

"He really is dead, believe me, I . . . "

"You just better stop drinking!"

"Do you want me to call you back in a little while? To see if you're okay?"

"I *said* I'm okay. I just don't believe it, and I don't want to talk, either."

"I'll call you back later."

"Yeah. Thanks. Goodbye."

I HANG UP THE PHONE TO STARE AT MY bedspread. Brown crushed velvet mountains and valleys. I will go down in there, I will . . . I pick up the phone and dial an all-night news station.

An officially hectic man answers. "Hello."

"Is Jim Morrison dead?" I wait for the guy to laugh. He doesn't.

"Yes. Jim Morrison died in Paris, Saturday." Mr. Matter-of-Fact minces no words.

"Oh," I choke loudly, "thanks," and hang up.

Something beyond disbelief convulses inside, flinging my body up and down. Tears break for screams. Screams in a muffled pillow, hidden deep inside, coming out,

"No, no, no," in exhaustion. "No," until it dies down. You should have known. The black sky has changed to grey dawn, and the moon is hanging above the tree branches. "Betraying moon, spinning world, why do you keep the breath in me?" I mutter, and more ceaseless conversation: "He just let the life slip out of him. It was his final rejection of this place. Why am I trapped in this cage, held captive in this punishing container? Life . . . I want out. Oh, won't you please just let me out?"

"You've gotta do it yourself."

"Just *let me out!*"

"Unmerciful!" I look at my wrists God dared make beautiful, white and bare.

"You want to cut your life line? Cut it!" I get up and walk to the front porch. Here I sit, watching the day rise. I can't do it. I have to live. And my wrists remain beautiful, white, unmarked.

CHAPTER 21

THE END

MY FACE IS ACHING TO MAINTAIN AN anonymous, inconspicuous dignity as the Métro approaches the cemetery. The people surging around my sides can't possibly know, but I think they do. Getting off at the Père Lachaise Métro stop, I feel embarrassed, and immediately suspect his spies are watching. That woman selling magazines and candy as I walk up the stairs, that man in the phony shoe repair shop. Shadows lurking in the alleys. They're all taking notes: Sunday, 2:00 P.M. . . . female, early twenties, print scarf covering reddish wisps, loose flowing blouse and jeans. If not American then Nordic, tall and thin, high cheekbones. Nervous, suspicious and real serious. . . . And I'm wondering would he recognize my description, would he recognize me walking here?

There's some French guy, old and mumbling, intent on distracting me. He's going on about his cigarette, cigarettes-in-general, or perhaps he's asking for a match and he'll give me a cigarette in return. Obscenity of sorts is leaking in via his damn unlit cigarette, waving madly through the air and chasing my many vehement no's. Even when I give my polished Lady-in-Mourning look at the cemetery steps, his relentless angry mumbling doesn't cease.

I scramble up the steps, with this now definite maniac panting after me, totally ruining my image. Reaching the top, I turn majestically cold and glare in righteous indignation. A cemetery guard sees us, and his mean look loaded with I-have-a-gun power hits the cigarette pervert. There are a few gruff words, and he retreats, shame-faced, down the stairs. Maybe he was a regular.

Mandatory rescue complete, the guard starts his routine. Babbling with frenzied gestures, he determines I'm American, yes, even a tourist. Terrific! Don't I need a map? They help you find what you're looking for. His map flashes strong and seductive. I watch him name off the dead famous people in wide mystic circles.

What's he think he's selling, joyride tickets? But okay, it's a big place. I give up, and feigning boredom, scrawl Morrison. Ah! He nods gleefully, yes, yes (of course) he's got them all memorized. Grinnning he draws lines over the treasure map, forming a significant rectangle and triumphant X to mark the spot. I thank him, reveling in the return of chivalry only to have him ask for money. You don't get a Xeroxed copy of the best French cemetery, containing geniuses of all dead shapes and colors for free! Why, even Edith Piaf is here. Stunned, I throw out two francs and flee. I try to hide this map; it feels almost decadent, with its names like listings in a gossip column, art gallery, library, or *Who's Who*. Further, it's incomprehensible. All I know is Jim's in part 5E of this miniature town with cobblestoned alleys and tiny streets leading up and around the myriad, ancient, rather ugly Houses of the Dead. They're like monk cells, pyramids, rusty, rain-eaten, jutting stiff and jagged lines to the sky. There's the new modern versions, shiny black marble slabs with sparkly silver flakes and ivory flowers, these never to wilt. Desperately, I hope he can't be in one of *those*.

Finally crossing a major intersection, I'm pleased. I have a sense of direction, after all. This pride fades when I notice the same guard actually balancing on one foot, sideways, leaning over to watch me. Yes, yes I confess, I'm dangerous, a potential grave robber. Only recently did I say, why don't they just dig up his damn grave and see if anything's down there, anyway? So you're right. Balance on your one foot sideways, lean over and intimidate me!

Guilty as hell over my thought crimes, I move quickly away from the scrutiny that's turned me red and awkward. Hiding behind a tree, breathing in slowly, I consult the rumpled map to realize I'm smack-dab in the middle of section 5E. Not that his makes things clearer. One wrong step and I'm lost again; I'll fall into section 1B. When I see *Jim* with an arrow engraved in the rust over my head, I'm not surprised. I follow the arrow and get lost. It must've been demonstrating some cosmic principle beyond Yin/Yang.

I'm angry now and decide I ought to rely on my psychic powers. This will be relatively hard, considering I can't believe he's dead or alive. Piercing French nearly cracking the air, and making the burial territory bizarrely foreign, belongs to three white-haired women. They're hunched over, shrilling and shrieking. I wait for them to leave, pretending I'm an historian for the fall of the sixties.

Soon, I enter. It's a regular graffiti environment, eight by four mausoleums thick, crammed full of multilingual phrases, epitaphs, and farsighted revelations, plus the regular ground graves. Just look at these outpourings of the collective unconscious, gathered here to salute one manifestation of their universal spirit, now flung compact, neat and complete into one dead body, revered, followed, worshipped and chased to his grave.

The mourners have left much for the casual viewer: "Jim was not a junkie; No hope without dope; Have a good trip in Père Lachaise; Fuck; You are immortal; My only love; Shit; Meet me at desert shore; Will you give me sanctuary? Wait for me; Is there room? Smoke grass; We all loved you; I'm coming soon; I'll never forget you; You and me forever; You were beautiful; You are beyond death."

MY DESCENT INTO THIS LAND HAS NOT been discreet. Nothing can stop the video camera recording each and every move to be minutely analyzed. Here at the rape site, the wheels spin and motors whir for tomorrow: She's circling round the grave, sniffing the air, looking offended, throwing her head back in disgust, shaking it in refusal. No on her lips, she circles more cautiously, a wild animal skirting the edges of safety. Her revulsion is transforming to anguish, even pain, as she shakes her head again, glaring in actual hatred at the scrawled words, then back down to what sacred thing has been defiled. She falls as drunk, weary against the other tombs, scraping her body close and hard as if to erase and smooth. *Away.* Now bending over, she gets the full view, an unmarked, but for a purple felt-pen transgression, ground grave, like a swimming-pool hole filled with yellow and white growing flowers. Only now she sees the crawling bugs. She stares intently, her body stiff and her face blank. She's furiously wiping her eyes, the tears filling them over and over again, stopping only to start. Betraying, she believes, something she wished not to believe.

I make the sign of the cross over my heart, though I come from no formal religion, but feel that gesture always, especially when seeing runover cats, dogs, and deer. And now I'm thinking, God bless you if you're dead, God bless you. Feeling bowled-over by such a confession, I look at this mess of a death. And all the needy greedy want, saying it's love, love, love, saying it's love and I don't know. I just have to leave. Leave before the bells around the tight pants belonging to some Parisian's get closer. There's a guy and two magenta haired girls with black fingernails, one is crying "Jim Morrison" in that soft "J" way. They pounce forward in hungry authority as I slink away, unnoticed. I give one backwards glance, my face again anguished and angry, partly for the camera, partly for me, but mostly for no one, nothing.

Soon I'm walking down another cobblestoned alley, leaving now is clean and clear. But I'm not looking up, something is plunging me down, down into the brownish black stone depths, and it feels so cool, like grass, all rushing up to me in rich muted tones. A blur is catching hold of me, stinging my eyes, the tears made soft though, with the repetitive chant: We all die, we all die, we all die. Then I'm on a street in the outside world, passing a flower shop, thinking, I should have bought some, thinking, I'm glad I didn't, we all die, we all die, we all die. I get on the Métro, and leave.

CHAPTER 22

TROUBLE CHILD

IDENTIFYING MARKS?" THE NURSE SAYS, in her soft, polite voice.

"What?"

"Do you have any identifying marks?"

"Oh." I touch my face. "These indentations here, by my nose – from chicken pox. And this shiny spot on my forehead from a rock . . . I think the light's wrong in here."

"Don't you have any birthmarks, any scars?" she says, her full lips pressed in and down.

"I have this." Proudly, shyly, I hold up my wrist. The meticulous series of cross-hatches forming a maroon Y over my blue veins doesn't look impressive anymore.

The nurse smiles sympathetically, as if I'd shown her a mangled rabbit's foot, and writes: "Distinquished by light freckles and auburn hair worn in bangs. Tall. Thin. Pretty." I put my arm back on the table and look away.

"The doctor said you were pretty, too," she says, glancing across the admitting room toward the ex-hippie who had interviewed me earlier. He'd made me feel I'd passed grueling entrance exams into an esoteric sanctuary.

"Really? Can I see?" Smiling, the nurse nods and pushes some papers toward me in a conspiratorial gesture. "Oh, he *did*. That was nice."

"Don't you think so?" she probes.

"I used to be . . . when I was young. I guess." I wonder if he'd just lied about taking acid in Griffith Park the same years as I.

"It says here you're only twenty-four."

"I know."

"That's young."

"Not for me," I remark, beginning to regret acting civil and sane to this woman. I have, after all, just been admitted to a mental hospital.

"You can change clothes now," a large black nurse says, thrusting a folded white smock toward me. There are two blue vinyl slippers on top.

"I don't have to. He said I wouldn't have to."

"Who?"

"Him." I point to the man who'd interviewed me.

"The doctor said that?"

I nod, reluctant to admit he is a doctor. She steams across the room. The other nurse grins at me and continues her paperwork.

I glance up at the skinny red second-hand of the institutional clock. The plastic dome covering the black, numbered hours is no longer transparent, but chipped, scarred, and greyed with age. I look back at my wrists and the neatly typed plastic bracelet stating my identity as an inmate of Ward 4-A.

THE SOFT RUBBER SOLES OF THE NURSE'S
shoes make a sure, gliding contact with the smoothly
worn floor; the light, squeaky noise echoes down the still
corridor. We walk past rows of rooms, some open, some
shut, each with a sliding window in the upper third of
the door. The windows are the same scuffed, translucent
plastic as the dome of the clock had been.

We stop before the glassed-in nurses station, and she
goes inside. I look around the corner and glimpse two
patients huddled in robes before a televison set.

"God, of all the things to do!" I seethe as the nurse
comes out into the hall.

"You mean the TV?" she asks, sounding defensive.
"Anyone can watch TV whenever they like here. Some
people can't sleep well, you know."

"Yeah, but that stuff helps put people here. They
grow up on it, that's why they can't sleep. It shouldn't
be here – everyone will just get sicker!"

"What are you, a model or something?" she asks,
calmy studying me.

"Who said that?"

"Your chart."

"I worked as a model, but I wasn't one. I was a painter,
but I didn't work as one," I answer.

"There's your daily schedule," she says, pointing to
the wall. A green felt-tip pen has divided an orange
construction-paper clock into neat sections. Each day is
to follow the same plan: wake-up, medication, breakfast,
large group, occupational therapy, lunch, rest, recrea-
tional therapy, dinner, snack, medication, sleep.

"Don't you want to go to bed now?" the nurse
inquires. "You must be tired."

"Oh, yeah, I guess so."

I follow her to a room, watch her stack my inspected possessions on the top shelf of a large metal locker, then crawl obediently into the small white bed. Pressing my head against the cool, flat pillow, I run my fingers over the nubby tufts in the light cotton bedspread and feel a sense of tranquility, of peace. After years of impossibility, I've finally admitted what I most feared – that I don't have control; am flawed, defeated, and ultimately helpless. Exhausted, I fall asleep. . . .

Jim's body is stretched out naked on a slab of stone, far beneath me. I spiral down, circle round and dive ever closer, a black crow over carrion. Reaching the ground, I stalk the boundaries of his open grave. I walk around and around, analyzing his body: the same skin – the fine, white translucency, the softness of his pores; the same delicate moulding – the precision of his hip bones, the slight, gentle contour of his stomach; the same hair – black, lustrous, lush against the white skin. The same detached, classic beauty has attained an inhuman perfection; it is cold, hollow, art. He is dead. . . .

Now I don't have to worry about living anymore. I have an orange chart with felt-tip rules to follow. Every morning a nurse will peer through my window, glide noiselessly to my bed, and slip a cool, glass thermometer from her silver tray into my mouth. It is perfect. Safe, in the heart of the lion, I sleep on.

THE FIRST MORNING I WAKE UP IN THE hospital, I see Jim at the foot of my bed. His face is radiant, surrounded by a silver-blue aura. I look up – and see his eyes are the world. Simultaneously blue, green, and brown, flecked with knowledge of everything, his

eyes are dead – and they are alive – looking steadily
through time into mine. Shining through death, they say,
"I love you. You will always love me."

His voice becomes as audible as bells, gently ringing.
"I forgive you," Jim says, shimmering and slowly dissolv-
ing back to the luminous blue transparency of dawn.

A DOORS DISCOGRAPHY

All recordings are released on Elektra Records.

TITLE AND RELEASE DATE	LABEL NUMBER
45 rpm Singles	
Break On Through / End of the Night (January 1967)	45611
Light My Fire / The Crystal Ship (April 1967)	45615
People Are Strange / Unhappy Girl (September 1967)	45621
Love Me Two Times / Moonlight Drive (November 1967)	45624
The Unknown Soldier / We Could Be So Good Together (March 1968)	45628
Hello, I Love You / Love Street (June 1968)	45635
Touch Me / Wild Child (December 1968)	45646
Wishful, Sinful / Who Scared You (February 1969)	45656
Tell All the People / Easy Ride (May 1969)	45663
Runnin' Blue / Do It (August 1969)	45675
You Make Me Real / Roadhouse Blues (March 1970)	45685

Love Her Madly / Don't Go No Farther
      (March 1971)   45726
Light My Fire / Love Me Two Times
      (April 1971)   45051
Touch Me / Hello, I Love You
      (April 1971)   45052
Riders on the Storm / The Changeling
      (June 1971)   45738
Riders on the Storm / Love Her Madly
      (September 1972)   45059
Roadhouse Blues / Albinoni Adagio
      (January 1979)   E-46005

$33^1/_3$ rpm Albums

"The Doors" (January 1967):   74007
Break On Through, Soul Kitchen, The Crystal Ship, Twentieth-Century Fox, Alabama Song, Light My Fire, Back Door Man, I Looked at You, End of the Night , Take It as It Comes, The End

"Strange Days" (October 1967):   74014
Strange Days, You're Lost Little Girl, Love Me Two Times, Unhappy Girl, Horse Latitudes, Moonlight Drive, People Are Strange, My Eyes Have Seen You, I Can't See Your Face in My Mind, When the Music's Over

"Waiting for the Sun" (July 1968):   74024
Hello, I Love You, Love Street, Not to Touch the Earth, Summer's Almost Gone, Wintertime Love, The Unknown Soldier, Spanish Caravan, My Wild Love, We Could Be So Good Together, Yes the River Knows, Five to One

"The Soft Parade" (July 1969):   75005
Tell All the People, Touch Me, Shaman's Blues, Do It, Easy Ride, Wild Child, Runnin' Blue, Wishful, Sinful, The Soft Parade

"Morrison Hotel" (February 1970):   75007
Roadhouse Blues, Waiting for the Sun, You Make Me Real,
Peace Frog, Blue Sunday, Ship of Fools, Land Ho!, The Spy,
Queen of the Highway, Indian Summer, Maggie M'Gill

"Absolutely Live" (July 1970):   2-9002
Who Do You Love, Medley: Alabama Song / Back Door
Man, Love Hides, Five to One, Build Me a Woman, When
the Music's Over, Close to You, Universal Mind, Break On
Through #2, The Celebration of the Lizard, Soul Kitchen

"13" (November 1970):   74079
Light My Fire, People Are Strange, Back Door Man,
Moonlight Drive, The Crystal Ship, Roadhouse Blues,
Touch Me, Love Me Two Times, You're Lost Little Girl,
Hello, I Love You, Wild Child, The Unknown Soldier

"L.A. Woman" (April 1971):   75011
The Changeling, Love Her Madly, Been Down So Long,
Cars Hiss by My Window, L.A. Woman, L'America, Hya-
cinth House, Crawling King Snake, The WASP, Riders on
the Storm

"Weird Scenes Inside the Gold Mine"
(January 1972):   2-6001
Break On Through, Strange Days, Shaman's Blues, Love
Street, Peace Frog, Blue Sunday, The WASP, End of the
Night, Love Her Madly, Spanish Caravan, Ship of Fools,
The Spy, The End, Take It as It Comes, Runnin' Blue, L.A.
Woman, Five to One, Who Scared You (You Need Meat),
Don't Go No Farther, Riders on the Storm, Maggie M'Gill,
Horse Latitudes, When the Music's Over

"The Best of the Doors" (August 1973):   EQ-5035
Who Do You Love, Soul Kitchen, Hello, I Love You, People
Are Strange, Riders on the Storm, Touch Me, Love Her
Madly, Love Me Two Times, Take It as It Comes, Moon-
light Drive, Light My Fire

"An American Prayer" (November 1978):   5E-502
Awake, To Come of Age, The Poet's Dreams, World on Fire,
An American Prayer, Roadhouse Blues, etc.